X-RAY REAL-TIME RADIOGRAPHY

AND IMAGE PROCESSING

Proceedings of a symposium held at Newbury, Berkshire in November 1988

Edited by

Dr R Halmshaw

Symposium organised by the British Institute of Non-Destructive Testing and hosted by Messrs Quantel Ltd

©1989 The British Institute of
Non-Destructive Testing

TA
417
.25
X73
1988

All rights reserved.
No part of this publication may be
reproduced, stored in a retrieval system
or transmitted in any form or by any means,
electronic, mechanical, photocopying,
recording or otherwise, without prior
permission in writing from
the publishers.

The British Institute of Non-Destructive Testing
1 Spencer Parade
Northampton NN1 5AA
Tel: 0604 30124 Telex: 31612 OTSSG Fax: 0604 231489

ISBN 0 903132 16 8

Printed by Chartwell Press Ltd
43 Chartwell Drive Wigston
Leicester LE8 2FS

BRUNEL UNIVERSITY
- - OCT 1992
LIBRARY

PREFACE

Methods of producing an X-ray image on a screen using a closed-circuit television camera to increase the image brightness have been known for many years. They have not, however, found many applications, due to the relatively poor image quality attained compared with film radiography.

The use of image digitization and a computer system for storage and image processing has re-awakened much interest in the process and it is clear that for many industrial applications of radiography a well-designed equipment can today produce images which compare closely with film images in quality. Developments in equipment design and new applications are advancing rapidly and this Symposium has attempted to be up-to-date with the state of the art in so far as commercial secrecy allows.

The equipment required is complex, containing several image transfer stages, and the individual components need to be carefully balanced to attain optimum performance.

In this Symposium there are several papers describing equipment design, discussing the various parameters involved, and detailing the attainable image sensitivity. Once the image is stored in digital form in a computer, it is available for a variety of additional processes beyond digital image enhancement.

Automatic flaw evaluation is possible and there are three papers on this topic.

Another paper indicates how stereoscopic X-ray images might be produced and by combining data from a scanning system, a fifth paper shows that tomographic images are possible from a real-time imaging equipment.

There are also related radiographic processes where a television-fluoroscopic image is used to produce measurements of internal component spacings, and another paper describes measurement of X-ray (Laue) diffraction patterns.

The Symposium was held at the Conference Centre, Quantel, Newbury. Quantel make digital image processing equipment suitable for use in real-time radiographic equipments and demonstrations were arranged during the Symposium.

R H

CONTENTS

X-RAY REAL-TIME RADIOGRAPHY - AN INTRODUCTION

Dr R HALMSHAW MBE

The various forms of X-ray television-fluoroscopic equipments (real-time radiography or radioscopy) now available are described, concentrating on newer systems using image digitisation and digital image processing.

Attempts to obtain high quality images suitable for butt-weld inspection, to be comparable with the image qualities required in film radiography of welds are discussed. Using a conventional wire-type image quality indicator, the IQI wire sensitivity attained can be closely similar to that required for normal-technique weld inspection, but it is argued that because of the larger unsharpness of most RTR images compared with film, this is an inadequate method of assessing image quality. It is suggested that additional measurements are needed, particularly of image unsharpness and image noise.

INTRODUCTION

The advent of X-ray image intensifier tubes in the early 1950s gave fluoroscopic methods a boost by enabling much brighter images to be obtained, but there were still serious limitations which prevented the method being widely used.

Later, X-ray image intensifier tubes were coupled to closed-circuit television cameras (CCTV), which produced a further increase in brightness, and more importantly also allowed the equipment to be used with high-energy X-rays and with higher output equipment without any serious problems of X-ray protection for the operator. The image was presented on a television monitor display screen which could be remote from the X-ray set and the intensifier.

In terms of flaw sensitivity performance, all these types of television-fluoroscopic equipments are usually much poorer than film, except perhaps with high-energy X-rays, principally because the primary image is formed on a poly-crystalline converter screen which

Consultant. 49 Crouch Croft, London SE9 3HX

has an inherently large image unsharpness. The development of methods which convert a television image into digital data, the digital framestore, and digital image processing have however produced great advances in the performance of television-fluoroscopic systems.

For those not familiar with the general concept, any image can be regarded as a series of very small elements - PIXELS - and the position and brightness of each pixel in the image area is determined and stored as digital data in a framestore. Commonly, an image is taken as 512 lines across an image, with 512 pixels on each line: ie the image is built up from $(512)^2$ = 262,144 spots. The brightness of each spot is measured on an 8-bit scale, ie 256 levels of brightness. Obviously the size of each pixel is a function of the overall image size - on a 300mm image each picture element will be 0.6mm wide (rather coarse), but on a 100mm image the pixel width is only 0.2mm.

EQUIPMENT

At present it seems possible to divide television-fluoroscopic equipments into three broad groups:-

Group 1 (Fig 1) A conversion screen is placed behind the specimen to convert the X-ray image (ie the X-rays transmitted through the specimen) to light. The screen is "open", not in a vacuum tube. The light image on this conversion screen is picked up by a closed-circuit television camera of suitable sensitivity, amplified, converted to digital data (pixels), and held in a framestore from where it can be extracted for image processing and display on a television monitor. Some CCTV cameras produce digital outputs directly without the use of an analogue-to-digital converter. The special point about Group 1 systems is that the primary conversion screen is open, and so it can be any size or type. However, because the image on this screen is usually of very low brightness, a very sensitive television camera is needed, usually one with an extra intensification stage, or an additional light amplifier.

Group 2 (Fig 2) A conventional X-ray image intensifier tube is used to convert the X-ray image to light (then to electrons and back to light) and a CCTV camera is focussed on the intensifier tube output screen. Because this output screen is much brighter than in Group 1 equipments a less sensitive CCTV camera can be used, and is almost always some type of vidicon. The output from the camera is amplified, digitised, stored, enhanced and displayed as with Group 1 equipment. The X-ray image is obviously limited to the X-ray intensifier screen size, which is commonly 6", 9", 12" diameter, although larger tubes exist. The inherent advantage of Group 2 equipments is that television vidicon cameras are stable and rugged items requiring little maintenance or adjustment.

Group 3 (Fig 3) A linear array of up to 1000 X-ray sensitive elements, each of the order of 1mm or less in width, can be constructed either using a piece of fluorescent screen covering a photodiode, or a

CCD device. If this is scanned across the specimen and the output of each element taken into a framestore, each position of the linear array is equivalent to one row of pixels: so that if several hundred rows are recorded and stored, the equivalent of a two-dimensional image is obtained, which can be enhanced, etc, and displayed. The scan time need only be a second or so, and this system is already in use in airport baggage search equipment.

The other development which may have applications in more than one of these groups is

PROJECTIVE MAGNIFICATION

If a microfocus X-ray tube is used and the detector screen is placed at a distance behind the specimen, the image of detail in the specimen is projected larger than true size on to the screen and, because of the very small source size, without any significant loss in image sharpness. Due to this projective magnification there is also a considerable reduction in the proportion of scattered radiation reaching the detector screen, which improves the contrast of the image. The magnification of the image means that the number of pixels on the screen image covers a smaller area of the specimen: ie in relation to specimen detail, the pixel size is smaller, therefore more image detail should be discernible. A simple calculation will illustrate this:-

The screen unsharpness of a typical fluorescent screen is 0.3mm and this will be the total unsharpness of the image if the specimen and detector screen are in close contact. From well-known geometric relationships, if a projective magnification M is used with a focal spot size s, the geometric unsharpness U_g is given by

$$U_g = s(M - 1)$$

but the true geometric unsharpness related to the image detail size is

$$U_T / M$$

U_T being the total unsharpness (a combination of the screen and geometric unsharpness).

If we have a 50 micrometre focus size and assume that because we are imaging on a screen with $U_s = 0.3$mm, we can make the value of $U_g = 0.2$mm without much affecting the total unsharpness (which will be 0.3mm), so the value of M can be calculated to be

$$0.2 = \frac{50}{1000}(M - 1) \qquad \underline{\text{so } M = 5}$$

and the true unsharpness related to specimen flaw size is 0.06mm (ie roughly the same as on a radiograph taken with 150kV X-rays on film).

The disadvantages of this method are, that to obtain a projective magnification of x5 the detector-specimen distance must be five times larger than the focus-to-specimen distance, which may be physically difficult. Also, the length of specimen examined at any one position is 1/5 of the length examined in a contact technique, which inevitably slows down the speed of inspection.

QUANTUM FLUCTUATION LIMITATIONS

There is a basic physical principle which should be mentioned at this stage. The X-ray image is formed from the X-ray quanta transmitted through the specimen and absorbed in the primary conversion screen. This screen usually absorbs only a small proportion of the X-ray quanta incident on it. Even if this primary image is formed from only a few quanta/mm^2/s on the screen, with intensifiers and CCTV it can still result in a bright final image because the amplification processes through the system are very large, but at the same time the quantum noise in this primary image will also be amplified. If therefore the image is produced from only a few X-ray quanta, the final image will be noisy, and this image noise will obscure image detail. The laws of quantum fluctuations are basic and cannot be changed: if there are N quanta/mm^2/s utilised on an image, the fluctuations (the noise) is $N^{\frac{1}{2}}$ and the signal-to-noise ratio is also $N^{\frac{1}{2}}$.

There are three ways of handling this problem:-

1. To devise a primary conversion screen which will absorb and convert a greater proportion of the incident X-ray quanta.
2. To use a higher output of X-rays or a higher than normal kilovoltage to get a higher intensity on the screen.
3. To integrate the signal over several seconds instead of using only the number of quanta absorbed in the time of one television frame: this can be done by a variety of methods in the image enhancement stage and is one of the most powerful arguments for using the digital system of image storage. If 25 frames are averaged, the time delay need still be only a little more than one second. If 100 frames are integrated, this is only about 4 seconds, and the time-delay in producing the image will be about 5 seconds. Pedantically the system is no longer "real-time", but probably the name will still be used.

This then is the "image noise" problem and it can be minimised by digital frame integration in the computer processing.

IMAGE UNSHARPNESS

All radiographic images are unsharp and the classic way of quantifying this is to measure the unsharpness width of the image of a physically sharp edge. In a television-fluoroscopic image there are various causes of unsharpness which need to be measured and combined:-

1. All X-ray-to-light conversion screens have a considerable unsharpness - typically at least 0.3mm.
2. The fact that the image is formed by means of a pixel matrix brings in another cause of unsharpness, whose size depends on how many pixels are used in relation to the length of the specimen which is imaged. 512 pixels to 100mm weld length means an unsharpness of 0.2mm.
3. The image is presented on a television line raster - standard systems being 625 lines. If the image is real-size on the television screen, there will be 625 lines for a 10" height of specimen, so one line-pair will be 0.4mm.

These three values would lead to a total unsharpness on the final image of 0.55mm - almost twice the unsharpness of the primary screen.

As already mentioned,one way round this problem is to arrange for the image to be larger than natural size on the screen, and one of the most powerful methods of doing this is to use a microfocus X-ray set with projective magnification. If using an X-ray set with a focal spot size of (say) 20 micrometres, and placing it close to the specimen with the detector screen at a distance so that the image is four times natural size, the geometric unsharpness will still be negligibly small. More importantly, as the image is enlarged the effect of the screen unsharpness in relation to the details in the specimen will be reduced in proportion to the image magnification, M.

The disadvantages of projective magnification are the necessity for an expensive microfocus X-ray set, and the need for the detector-to-specimen distance to be equal to

focal spot-to-specimen distance . M

which may be physically difficult or lead to very long exposure-times.

IMAGE CONTRAST

The third factor in image quality is contrast. Again, the use of image digitisation and a framestore make the modification of image contrast relatively easy. There are a number of contrast enhancement programmes both for overall enhancement and for local enhancement.

IMAGE QUALITY

In any T-F system the image is displayed on a television monitor on a line raster. This is a completely different nature of an image to that on a radiographic film, which usually has a grain structure barely visible without some magnification.

It is not therefore by any means certain that conventional IQI such as wires will give a fair or comparable representation of image quality. For example, in welds the most serious potential defect is the small crack, and it is not yet at all clear how well such defects will be imaged on a TV screen, even if shown at several times natural size. One would like to know whether, when the wire IQI sensitivity is the same on a television image and on film, the flaw sensitivity can also be equated for different types of flaws. Calculations of flaw sensitivity suggest that this is not so, and that wire IQI sensitivity is not a satisfactory method of assessing the performance of a television-fluoroscopic imaging system. In particular, it appears possible to have an apparently good IQI sensitivity and at the same time a poor crack sensitivity.

Theoretical studies of radiographic sensitivity show that wire IQI sensitivity is strongly dependant on contrast parameters, whereas crack sensitivity is much more dependant on the size of the image unsharpness, which is, as has already been shown, comparatively large with present-day XRTI equipments.

It is therefore recommended that in applications where a high sensitivity is required for planar flaws such as cracks, lack of fusion, narrow lack of penetration in welds, that the criterion of satisfactory image quality must be more than a conventional wire or hole IQI sensitivity value. An additional measure of image sharpness is required. This can be provided conveniently by the image of a duplex wire IQI, such as type IIIA in BS:3971:1985.

This image unsharpness limitation can be completely overcome by the use of a projectively magnified image, but this necessitates the use of a microfocus X-ray source. Some improvement in image quality can be obtained with the use of a minifocus X-ray source together with a small amount of projective magnification, and this seems at present to be the best practical compromise solution for equipment to be used on a welding site outside the laboratory.

FLAW SENSITIVITY

Well-established formulae for crack, step, wire and hole sensitivity on film can be modified for television-fluoroscopic systems by incorporating image magnification as an extra parameter and assuming that image noise can be eliminated by television-frame integration. The numerical values of some of the parameters are not so certain as in the case of film radiography, but the major importance of total image unsharpness on attainable crack sensitivity is very clearly shown. (Fig 4).

At present the unsharpness of an RTR equipment can only be overcome by projective magnification. Contrast can be adjusted over wide limits with digital image processing, although to get an overall contrast increase of x5 (to match the film gradient of G = 5) is not easy without a large increase in noise.

CONCLUSIONS

It is noteworthy that practically no data has yet been published on RTR system performance in terms of real defects such as cracks, etc. and the calculations of crack sensitivity suggest that the larger unsharpness of an RTR system would make it much poorer than film, even though similar wire IQI values can be obtained.

I believe the duplex wire IQI has a lot of merit for the assessment of television-fluoroscopic systems. It certainly measures unsharpness and resolution, but one would like to know how it responds to system noise.

Formulae can be developed by which theoretical crack and hole sensitivity can be calculated in terms of the radiographic parameters of contrast and unsharpness, on the assumption that image noise can be eliminated. Although the application of these formulae to television-fluoroscopic systems requires considerable extrapolation, they indicate very strongly the importance of image unsharpness in crack sensitivity.

By frame integration the noise can be reduced to acceptable levels, but at the end one has an image on a television screen, on a line raster, within the brightness range which a display monitor is capable of handling, and this is a very different presentation to a film radiograph on a viewing screen.

I have deliberately left most of the subject of digital image processing and its influence on discernible flaw sensitivity to other speakers. The subject is developing very rapidly and serious thought is already being given to automatic flaw recognition through computer-generated data.

I am quite certain that RTR has many potential new applications, and obviously automatic pattern recognition systems will be developed in the future, but I do not believe that RTR is yet a replacement for all film radiography.

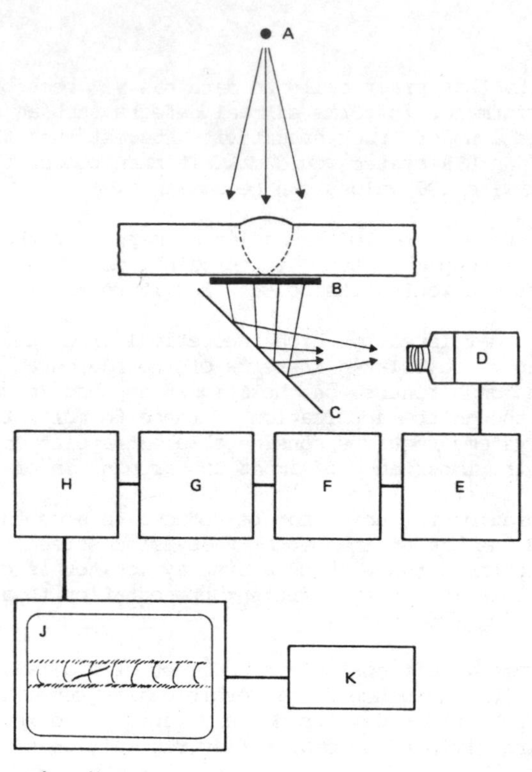

A – X-ray source
B – conversions screen
C – mirror
D – television camera with extra intensification stage
E – analogue-to-digital convertor
F – framestore
G – computer
H – digital image processing
J – display monitor
K – video recorder

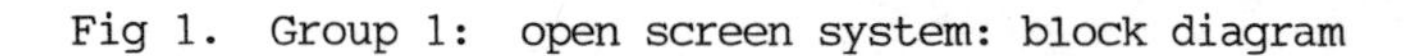

Fig 1. Group 1: open screen system: block diagram

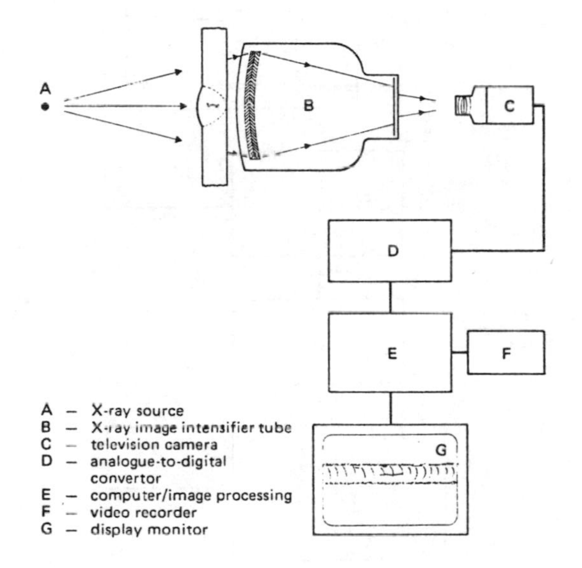

Fig 2. Group 2: image intensifier tube system: block diagram

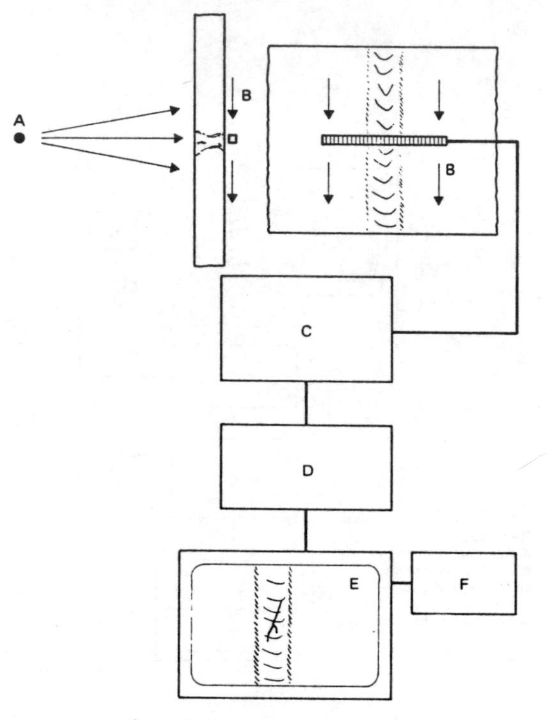

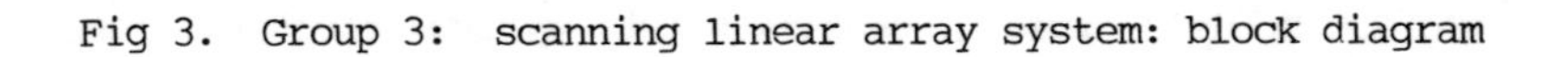
Fig 3. Group 3: scanning linear array system: block diagram

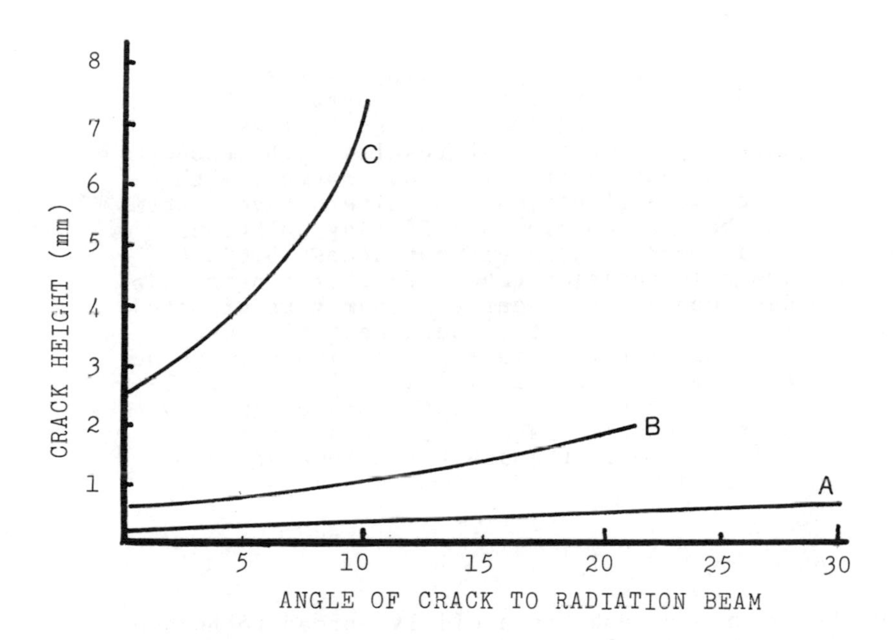

Fig 4. Calculated crack sensitivities for a crack of opening width 0.125mm.

A - fine-grain film technique
B - television-fluoroscopic equipment with minifocus X-rays (0.2mm) and x3 projective magnification
C - television fluoroscopic equipment with no projective magnification.

PROGRESS IN REAL-TIME RADIOGRAPHY

R. Grimm

SUMMARY

Comparing the different imaging systems available for real-time radiography, the most widely used image intensifier systems indeed provide optimal results with respect to contrast and resolution. However, with specific applications the alternative systems may become superior by offering solutions to inspection problems not accessible with image intensifier tubes. Further progress in development of linear arrays may be expected and will improve the usefulness of these imaging systems. Image processing has become an important tool in industrial X-ray real-time inspection, offering improved quality of radioscopic images. Its main future perspective is the use for automated image evaluation.

INTRODUCTION

Real-time radiography is a widely spread technique. Various types of electronic imaging systems are used to produce the X-ray irradiation images of the inspected objects. Three different system types are most commonly used. All of them offer an easy way of automized inspection procedures. During the recent past, real-time radiography has gained higher importance in X-ray inspection. New fields of application of this technique have been introduced.

The main impact in real-time radiography resulted from the improved technology of the systems using image intensifier tubes and from the possibility to improve image quality by noise reduction and image processing. Another

ISOTOPEN-TECHNIK DR. SAUERWEIN GMBH, D-5657 Haan 1

important factor has been the availability of X-ray tubes with small focal spot sizes, which can be used to improve spatial resolution by geometrical magnification.

Fluorescent screen type systems have been the first systems used in filmless X-ray inspection. They offer a higher degree of freedom with respect to system design and selection of system components optimized for the specific application. The third type using linear detector arrays is well known from luggage inspection systems. These detector arrays are now available with smaller pixel sizes offering improved spatial resolution.

FLUOROSCOPIC INSPECTION SYSTEMS

The two main components of fluorescent screen systems as schematically depicted in fig 1, are the fluorescent screen itself converting the X-rays to visible light and a low light level TV camera. As the amount of light produced by the screens is extremely low, a standard TV camera is not useful. In addition a mirror is very often used to deflect the screen image and remove the camera off the direction of the incident X-ray beam.

Fluorescent screen systems are also named "open" systems, an indication one of their main advantages, i.e. system components are accessible and interchangeable for varying applications. Problem-oriented selection of fluorescent screens is possible. One of our main aims in this area was a careful study of system components available to optimize a system for operation in the low energy range. From our experience, the best results with respect to the TV camera are obtained with a vidicon type of tube and a single-stage light amplifier in front of the tube target. This has been found sufficient with respect to light amplification, avoiding the significant introduction of additional electronic noise and decreased resolution by a second stage.

Additionally, a large number of different screens, including rare earth screens, scintillator crystals and scintillating fibre optical systems have been tested. The comparison was done under identical conditions for each screen and revealed very large differences in light conversion rate, contrast and spatial resolution. The contrast has been characterized by the wire IQI sensitivities, spatial resolution has been measured using the CERL duplex wire penetrameter on the imaged material. Contrast and resolution values differ by up to two IQI wires or CERL wire-pairs respectively. These results emphasize the requirement to optimize the system components carefully for each specific applications.

Apart from these studies of the main components of a fluorescent screen system, we additionally evaluated the results obtainable for wire IQI sensitivity and resolution for a specifically designed imaging system. The results for a system using tapered fibre optics, a microchannel plate and a camera are shown in fig.2.
With the camera and fibre optical system the fluorescent screen is coupled to the fibre optics cone, and at the other end of this cone is the TV camera. Because of the conical shape of the fibre optical coupler, the image on the fluorescent screen is reduced in diameter to the pick-up tube size. The entrance size of the fibre optics is 75 mm. Coupling the fluorescent screen to a microchannel plate produces some amplification of the converted light so that a conventional TV camera can be used to pick up the image at the output screen.

Two examples can demonstrate the high degree of freedom in design of the imaging system. Crankshaft bearings of aluminium engines are to be examined for porosity.
It is necessary for the imaging system to be placed inside a narrow space of apprx. 60 x 110 x 70 mm, between the individual walls of the specimen. This problem can be successfully solved by the use of a fluorescent screen system specially designed to fit into this space. The image at the trapezoidal screen is deflected by a prism on to the TV camera. The imaging system is moved in parallel to the X-ray tube by a programmed manipulator, fig.3. The system uses a microfocus X-ray tube, to reduce the geometrical unsharpness.

The second system has been designed for the inspection of conveyor belts in coal mines operating at 3 - 4 metres/s. The rugged system shown in fig.4 is equipped with a very large fluorescent screen of 30 x 40 cm. For reasons of motion unsharpness, an X-ray flash tube is used. This tube can operate at 8 to 15 flashes per second, each one with a pulse length of 20 nanoseconds and an intensity (tube current) of 600 A. It is not possible for an inspector to follow up individual images of the belt. Typically, ten images per second are recorded on a VCR including a belt position encoding within each image. Viewing the video tape in slow motion, a 100% inspection of the conveyor is done.

COMPUTERIZED REAL-TIME RADIOGRAPHY

We have devised a radioscopic system GAMMASCOPE GS220 for an useful energy range starting as low as 15 kV X-ray energy and extending up to 15 MeV of linear accelerators (1). The system comprises an image converter as used in modern medical X-ray television systems. However, the thickness of the CsI screen has been substantially increased without anyessential deterioration in spatial resolution. The amplified image at the phosphor screenis transmitted to the target of the TV-tube using high quality, focussing optical system. The TV camera and the TV-tube are specially selected, resulting in an overall optimized TV-signal.

Notwithstanding the increase in detection efficiency resulting from the relatively thick entrance screen, the image on the phosphor screen still suffers from significant noise. An improvement of the signal-to-noise ratio as well as further image improvements can be obtained by using an image processing system. In analogy to film-radiography where long-time exposure is usual, the image processing system must be able to sum up a lot of subsequent TV-images. Typical summation times range from a few seconds up to a maximum of 1 minute for isotopes such as Co-60. The contrast sensitivity of this system is given in fig 5. It has been measured using wire type IQI's placed on the source side of the sample. The radioscopic images were taken without any geometrical magnification. As radiation sources we have used X-ray tubes as well as isotope sources and linear accelerators. The results are compared with the image quality classification (dashed lines) as defined by the German standard (DIN 54109).

Noise reduction of the image is the first and most important step. All successive processing techniques only serve to improve the presentation of the information which is contained within the original image (c.f.fig 6) Most techniques can be performed within a few seconds and are used to facilitate detection of defects by an examiner. They also provide a digital representation of the image which can be used for computer-supported evaluation, e.g. of defect sizes or depths, or for automated computerized evaluation of the image. An increasing number of inspection systems at production lines is semi-automated, i.e. the handling of the samples, the x-ray tube, the radioscopic image acquisition and image processing is automated and controlled by a central computer. The first step in automation of the system is the radioscopic image acquisition, and image processing is automated and controlled by a central computer. The final step in automation of the system is the automated defect evaluation. The problem is not yet completely solved, but a very promising outlook is given by works of two other research institutes (2) (3). In collaboration with other institutions we have written an algorithm which is able to apply these procedures to digitized radiographs using GAMMASCOPE CRTR. The results are encouraging, one example showing the various steps involved is displayed in fig 7.

One of the limitations of real-time systems arises from the comparatively high system unsharpness. This problem can be overcome by geometrical magnification, which is possible by using a mini- or micro-focus X-ray tube. Microfocus X-ray tubes have a very small focal spot size, which can be less than 10 microns in diameter, depending on the kilovoltage and tube current. Due to the very small focal spot, they permit one to use a large geometrical magnification without geometrical unsharpness, so improving the spatial resolution. A clear disadvantage of using a large geometrical magnification is the smaller display size with respect to the object size. Apart from inspection of e.g. microchips and other small parts there are industrial installations for weld inspection using high geometrical magnification (up to l0-fold) e.g. inspection of laser or electron beam welded seams on thin steel sheets. For standard display size of the real-time system without geometrical magnification, i.e. 220 mm diameter of input screen, the 625-lines TV-system will show up an unsharpness of 0.5 mm. The total unsharpness is 0.25mm for 2-fold and 0.1 mm for 6-fold geometrical magnification, respectively.

The larger number of industrial inspection systems use only a limited magnification for reasons of total inspection time. For many applications a magnification of 2 - 3 is sufficient to show up clearly all types of defects involved. For this limited range of magnification, X-ray tubes of focal spot size 0.2 to 0.4 mm (minifocus) can be utilized. Apart from improving the system resolution, also the contrast sensitivity is increased. These results will be published elsewhere. As an example for 10 mm of steel thickness, image quality class 1 requests a sensitivity of 1.6% and for 30 mm of steel of 1.1%. These values are obtained with our system without geometrical magnification. Using geometrical magnification of 1.5 to 2 these values improve to 1% and 0.7% respectively, for processed images.

HIGH RESOLUTION LINEAR SCANNING SYSTEM GAMMASCAN D25

Linear scanning systems are well known from luggage inspection at airports. They utilize detector arrays of pixel sizes of typically 1 mm or even larger. For applications in nondestructive testing in most cases a better resolution is required. The development of CCD and photodiode arrays has led to light sensitive linear arrays of pixel sizes down to the range of some ten microns. In many cases the pixels are not square but rectangular-shaped with the small dimensions across the array. The dimension in the perpendicular direction is in general much larger and defined by the opening of the collimator used. A scanning system has been devised using a linear array of 1024 pixels of size 0.025 mm by 3 mm. The array has been coupled via fibre optics to a fluorescent screen for conversion of X-rays to light. The linear array is cooled by a Peletier element to reduce the electronic noise. Scanning widths other than 25 mm can be obtained by using detector arrays which are available with pixel numbers from 64 to 4096. Radiation images of high contrast and an unsharpness of 0.1 mm could be obtained without any geometrical enlargement and using a X-ray focal spot size of 3 x 3 mm. As an example, the image of a steel weld is displayed in fig 8.

A slit collimator in front of the entrance screen is used to reduce the horizontal pixel size. The opening of this collimator slit and the scanning speed determine the vertical resolution. The object is moved across the array by a high precision manipulator. The whole system (c.f. fig 9) is controlled by a DEC computer. Prior to storing the data in a framebuffer for display on a TV monitor, a preprocessing is done. Intensity fluctuations as measured by a reference detector and variations in the individual pixel sensitivities are compensated. For further image processing or evaluation, the system can be upgraded by a fast image processor. All standard types of digital data storage like magtapes and discs are available.

One of the main limitations with respect to the use in X-ray inspection systems results from the very low scanning speeds obtainable with thee high resolution detectors. Additionally, the useful energy range is strongly limited. From practical considerations the newly available arrays of 0.4 and even 0.2 mm pixel size appear to be much more promising.

(1) Link, R.; Nuding, W.; Sauerwein, K.
The British Journal of Non-Destructive Testing (July 1984)

(2) Keck, R.; Coen, G.
Zerstörungsfreie Materialprüfung, QZ 32/33 (1987)

(3) Daum, W.; Rose, P.; Heidt, H.; Builtjes, J.H.
British Journal of NDT Vol. 29/1987

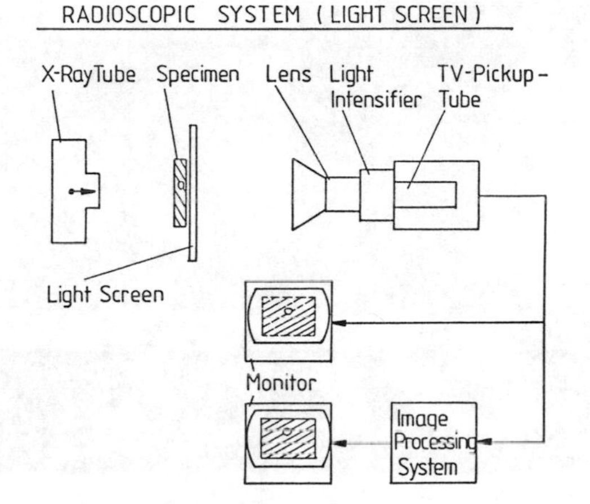

Fig 1: Scheme of Fluoroscopic Imaging System

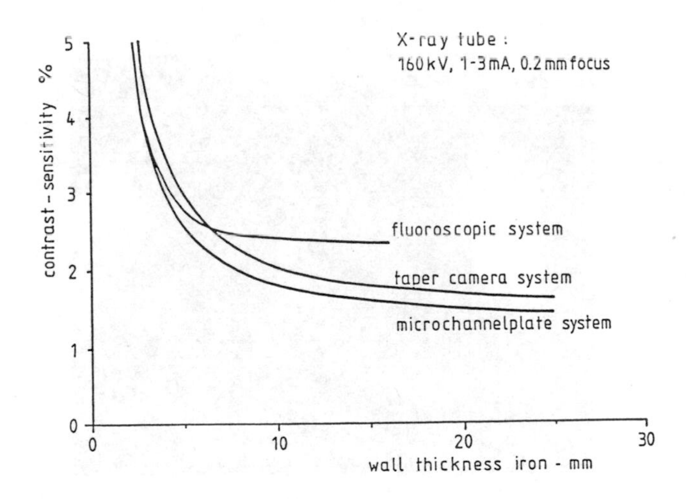

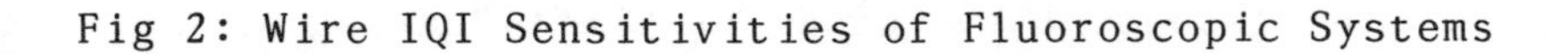
Fig 2: Wire IQI Sensitivities of Fluoroscopic Systems

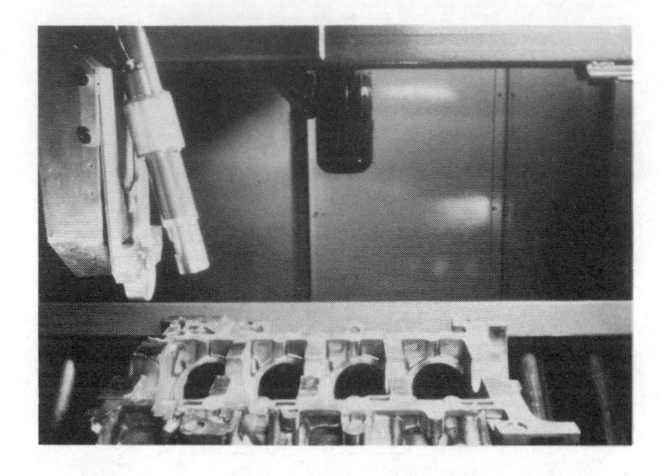

Fig 3a: Aluminum Engine Inspection System

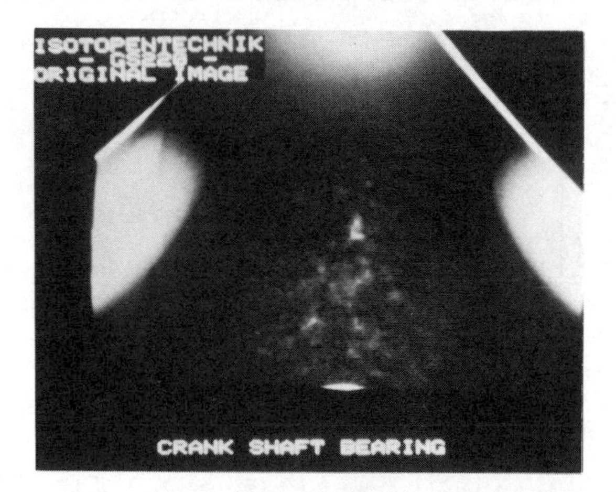

Fig 3b: Fluoroscopic Image of Crank Shaft Bearing Area

Fig 4: Detailed View of Conveyor Belt Inspection System

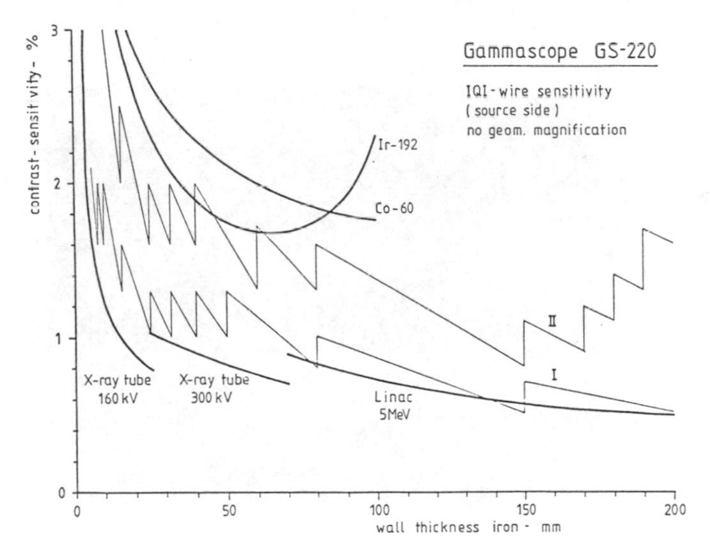

Fig 5: Wire IQI Sensitivities of Image Intensifier System for Different X-ray Sources

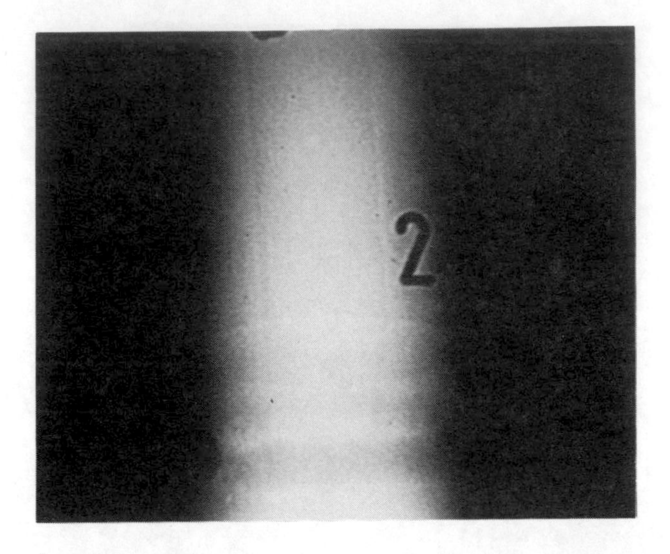

Fig 6a: Radioscopic Image of Circumferential Weld (real-time)

Fig 6b: Radioscopic Image of Circumferential Weld (Processed)

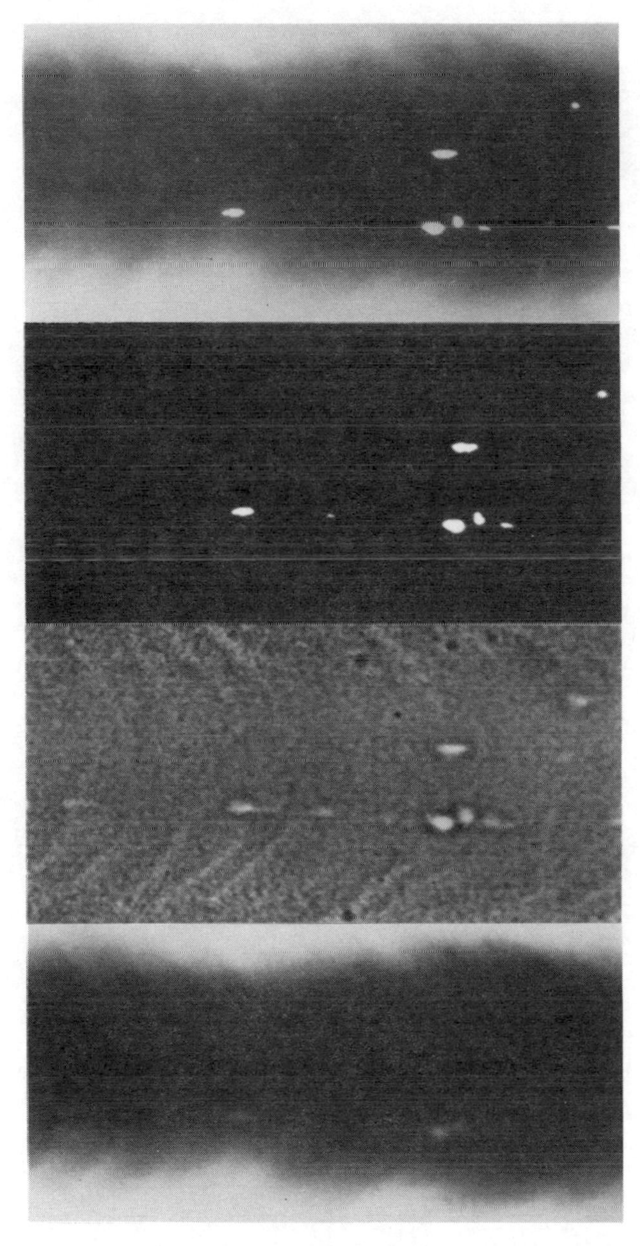

Fig 7. Automated Evaluation of Radioscopic Weld Image.

Fig 8: GAMMASCAN D25 Image of a Laser Weld in a 1 mm Steel Sheet

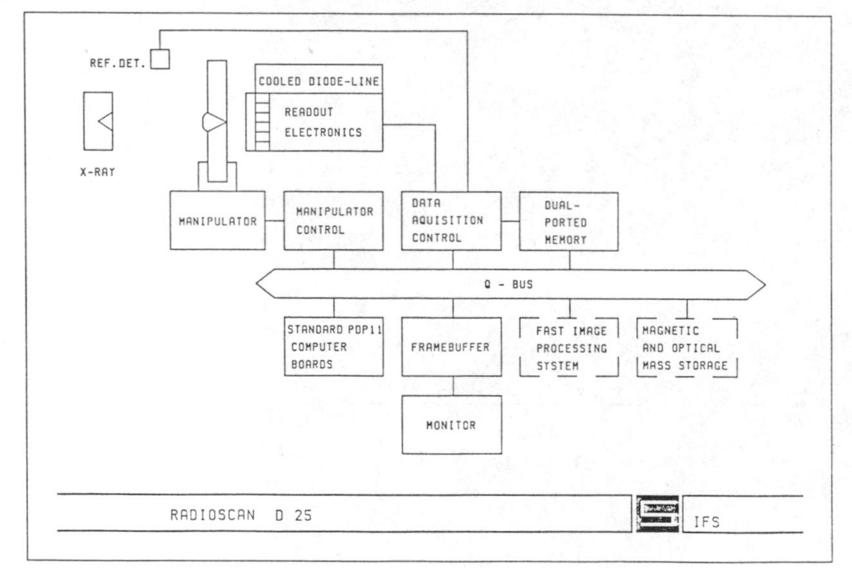

Fig 9: Schematic Diagram of High Resolution Scanning System GAMMASCAN D25

ADVANTAGES OF THE IMAGE PROCESSING SYSTEMS IN INDUSTRIAL REAL-TIME RADIOGRAPHY.

ERNEST E.BABYLAS

ABSTRACT

An image intensifier operating with a closed-circuit television camera offers outstanding results with respect to sensitivity, contrast, definition, signal/noise ratio and absence of lag. To further improve image quality, successful use has been made of an image enhancement device. A substantial improvement in image quality can be effected merely by increasing contrast. Modification of photon flux level at the detector face-plate, together with frame integration improves image contrast and reduces noise phenomena.

Factors linked with image definition are also analysed. Picture distortion can be controlled using spatial filters.

Results are presented based on IQI values, and industrial applications in foundries, welding and defence are described.

INTRODUCTION

The obvious advantage of real-time X-ray control is that the results are displayed during irradiation of the object, so that when the quality observed deviates from an established standard immediate action can be taken with respect to the means of production.

The basic principles of this method are substantially the same as those of conventional radiographic examination and imply processing of an image obtained using the transmittance properties of the object under control.

Several means have been developed in order to obtain immediate examination results. The object of this paper however, is not a comparison of the various capabilities and limits of these different detection means. Other publications such as ASTM 1000-84 (1) or IIW Progress Report (2) deal with this subject.

After selecting a detection system, we have tried to show how one can increase the quality of results obtained, using an image processing system.

2. DETECTOR SYSTEM SELECTED

Balteau S.A. Herve, Belgium.

The fluoroscopic examination technique uses the property of ionizing radiation of causing fluorescence of certain salts, so that the beam modulated by the object under examination is made visible by means of light emission. Although this discovery is contemporaneous with the discovery of X-radiation, the use of this property for industrial control has remained limited. The main reason being that, in terms of quality, up to now, fluoroscopy did not offer satisfactory results compared with those achieved by means of photographic emulsions.

However, the development of high-performance detectors, the evolution of television pick-up tubes and the innovative steps in the field of image processing using high-activity electronic means leads us to reconsider our point of view.

2.1. SELECTION CRITERIA OF A FLUOROSCOPIC DETECTOR

In order to reach quality standards which compare favourably with those obtained using X-ray films for instance, a fluoroscopic detector should have a series of characteristics which meet the following selection criteria.

- Sensitivity : concerns the quantity of energy required for checking a given thickness of a specific material.

- Resolution : the capacity of the detector to produce a clear or sharp image of a small detail.

- Contrast : the capacity of the detector to display a small variation of radiation intensity detected, through an obvious image difference.

- Signal-to-noise ratio : concerns the capacity of the detector to display an image lacking random fluctuations within the complete image.

- No time-lag.

In fact, the great advantage of real-time examination is that the object can be examined while it is in motion, so that the most favourable angle of incidence can be selected in order to detect material flaws, while the object motion does not affect examination quality.
Up to now the detector which best meets these five criteria is the image intensifier used with a television system.

This being specified, treatments described below in order to improve image quality may also be applied to other types of detectors. Besides, some detectors may offer a specific superiority over any of the selection parameters.

3. IMAGE INTENSIFIER

As mentioned above, data detection is based on the principle of light emission from a fluorescent salt. The image intensifier has two functions: on the one hand to show, by way of light emission, the different intensities of radiation, and to provide an image having an intensity several thousand times higher than that of the initial image formed on the detector element.

3.1. FUNCTIONAL PRINCIPLE OF THE IMAGE INTENSIFIER

The image intensifier is an electron tube derived from a visible light intensifier.

Under the effect of X- or gamma-radiation, the input screen produces light quanta for each photon absorbed by the fluorescent layer of the screen. A photocathode located directly behind the input screen releases electrons under the effect of the light photons from the input screen.

By adequate electrostatic focussing and due to the acceleration effect created by the positive potential of the anode, the electrons released by the photocathode form the final image observed on a smaller diameter output screen.

The combined effect of electron acceleration and of output screen surface reduction provides the light gain within the image intensifier.

3.2. EVOLUTION OF IMAGE INTENSIFIERS

Introduced in the 1950's, image intensifiers have known several development stages. Originally, the diameter of the input screen was 12cm (4.7inches), light gain was 800 and the fluorescent screen was made of a mixture of zinc sulphide and cadmium sulphide.

By the end of the 1950's, the diameter of the input screen was raised to 21cm (8.3inches) and light gain increased to 3000, so that observation of the output screen using a vidicon tube camera became possible.

By the end of the 1960's, the introduction of cesium iodide used as a detector element in the construction of image intensifiers offered a 35% sensitivity increase with respect to zinc sulphide.

Cesium iodide produced in the shape of very thin needles prevents lateral scattering of light and increases the chances of interaction between the X photons and the cesium iodide needles arranged parallel to the path of the X photons.

Further developments also include computer calculation of the electronic optical system, development of variable magnification means, providing a zoom function and adaptation of the output screen in order to allow image transmission without any loss to the television camera.

3.3. QUALITY ACHIEVED WITH AN IMAGE INTENSIFIER

Quality achieved with the different detector systems can be measured using wire or hole-type image quality indicators.

The following diagram (Fig.1) shows the results obtained using a fluoroscopic system containing an image intensifier and those obtained using a photographic emulsion. The IQI sensitivity obtained with the image intensifier is poorer than that obtained with a film by a factor of approx. 2.

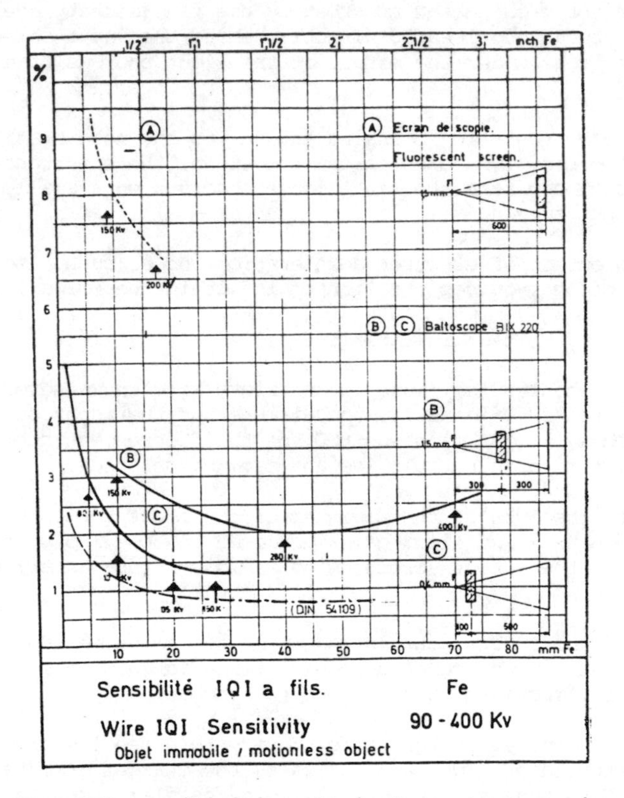

Fig.1. Wire IQI sensitivities attained on steel specimens.

We found it quite interesting to try and find out the reasons for this quality difference in order to find the most efficient means to achieve quality results which compare favourably with those reached using photographic emulsions.

3.4. STRUCTURE OF THE DETECTOR ELEMENT

The conversion factor of X-radiation energy into light energy intimately depends on the basic grain size of the detector. In order to increase the conversion power, the interaction between the X-photons and the detector has to be increased either by increasing the absorption level or by increasing detector grain size.

Elements with a high atomic number should be selected in preference to any other. Further, selection of detector grain size is rather limited as a larger grain size is not capable of discriminating two events occurring close to one another and reduces spatial resolution.

A limited resolution is often found to be the main reason for a loss of quality. The following values are indeed obtained when comparing the resolution power of a film with that of a fluoroscopic detector:

PHOTOGRAPHIC EMULSION	180 lp/mm
FLUOROSCOPIC SYSTEM	8 lp/mm

In the list of factors affecting image quality, the resolving power is not necessarily the main factor found to limit the efficiency of the examination system.

The following table gives the main factors conducive to image quality:

Table 1.

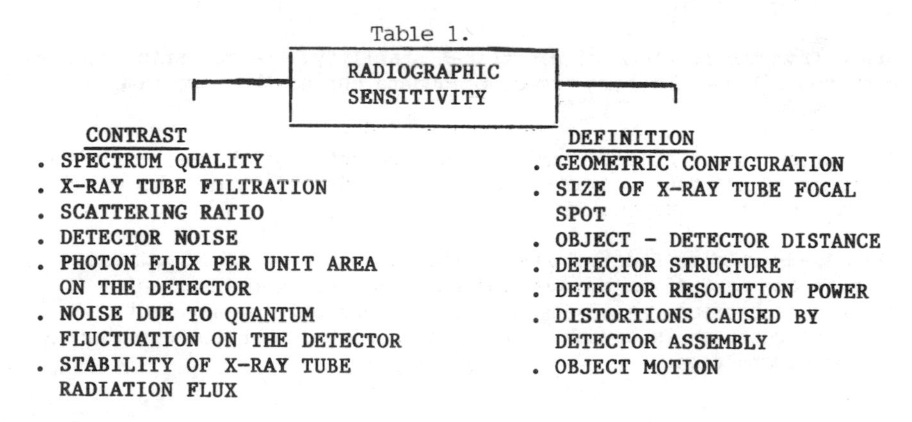

With reference to the charts giving the obtained IQI sensitivity related to penetrated thickness, the following conclusion may be drawn when comparing the established steel and aluminium penetration charts.

The following results, as given in Table 2 below, are obtained in the case of corresponding thicknesses, test conditions and detectors:

Table 2.

Thickness	Steel		Aluminium		Ratio	
	IQI Sensit.	kV	IQI Sensit.	kV	Sensit.	kV
5	3	80	2.5	40	1.2	2
10	2.1	100	1.8	45	1.16	2.2
15	1.7	120	1.3	50	1.3	2.4
20	1.45	135	1.2	53	1.2	2.54
25	1.4	150	1.1	55	1.27	2.7
30	1.4	160	1	60	1.4	2.6

The reason why contrast is obviously higher in case of aluminium than in the case of steel is to be found in the kV and scattered radiation values.

In other words, if the contrast of the image could be brought to the same value in the case of steel as that of aluminium, the image sharpness and resolution power parameters should not prevent one from achieving a better quality, since it is already secured in the case of aluminium.

4. IMAGE CONTRAST FACTORS

4.1. QUANTUM ASPECT

Apart from the problems of electrical stability, the radiation source does not release the same number of quanta during the same time intervals.

Absorption in the object examined and interaction with the sensitive elements of the detector are also phenomena dependent on laws of statistics, thus varying with time.

This leads to some fluctuations of the intensity of light emitted, even in the case of an homogeneous exposure. Further, brightness difference between two adjacent areas is perceptible only provided that its contrast is approx. 3 to 5 times higher than the contrast of random fluctuation.

4.2. PHOTON DENSITY PER UNIT AREA

Perception or non-perception of a small detail depends on the density of photons received per detector unit area. Rose (3) established a relation showing that contrast, photon density and diameter of any perceptible detail are interlinked.

In the following diagram, (Fig.2), this relation shows that in order to be visible, the contrast of 1mm diameter detail should be 40% if the photon flux is 10^2 photons/mm^2, whereas its contrast may be only 0.15% if the photon flux is 10^6 photons/mm^2.

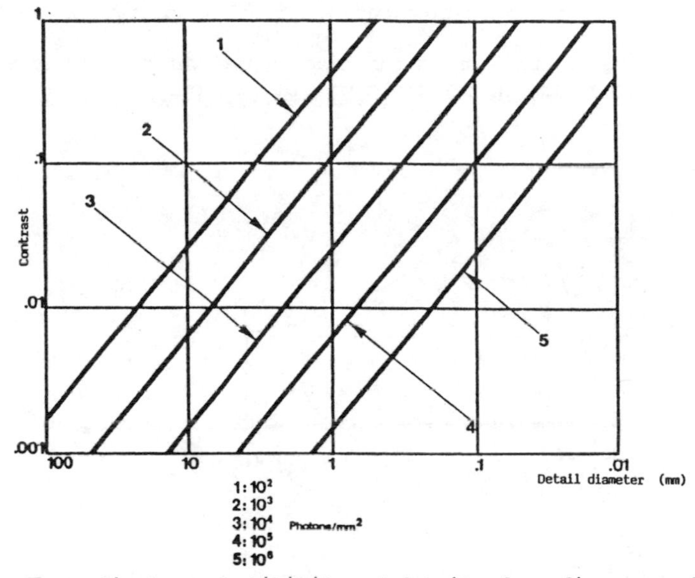

Fig.2. Theoretical perceptibility of details depending on number of photons.

A high photon flux at the detector should therefore be available in order to display extremely small details offering a low contrast.

A radiation source with a high flux density is accordingly preferable. Further, the detector-radiation source distance should be kept as short as possible.

As a rule, X-radiation and gamma radiation may be used for fluoroscopic examination. The photon flux is however much greater in the case of X-radiation sources than with radioisotopes.

The following values are generally encountered:

Source	Photon flux at 1m
140kV X-rays: 1mA	4.55 10^7 photons/mm^2.s
10 Ci Cobalt-60	6.10^4 " "

4.3. PHOTON FLUX INCREASE BY MEANS OF TUBE CURRENT INCREASE

Modern X-ray generators offer the possibility of operating at maximum output. The microprocessor built into the control unit allows easy programming of the X-ray tube load curves, so that maximum tube current can be obtained for each high voltage value selected, taking into account heat dissipation capability of a specific X-ray tube.

The following Figure 3 shows the load curves which apply to an X-ray tube in current use in the field of fluoroscopy.

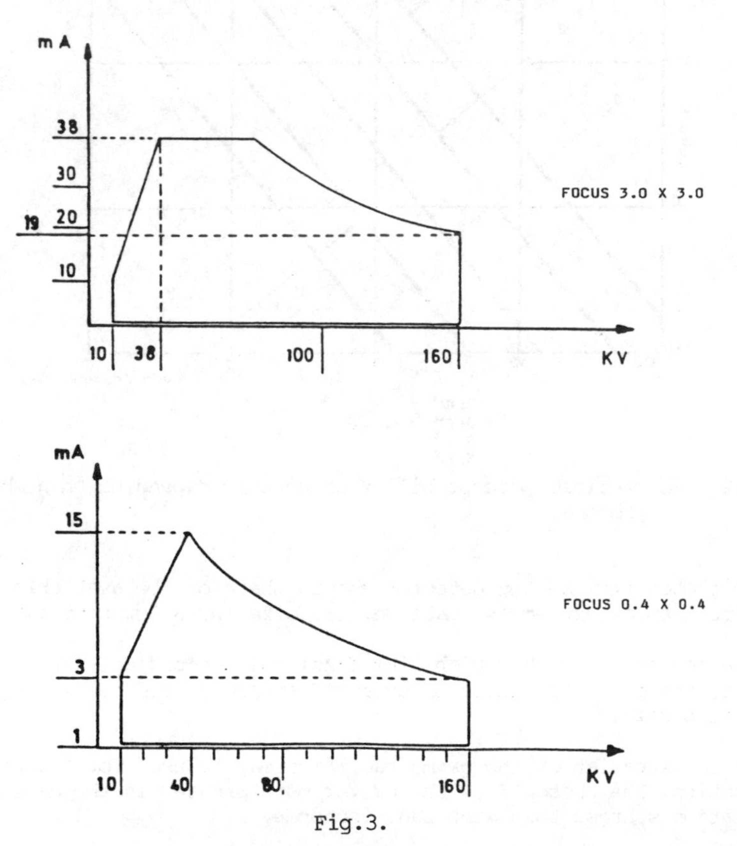

Fig.3.

As far as the electrical signal transmitted to the television camera of the detector system is concerned, an image is collected every 0.04s. Random fluctuations of brightness cause noise superimposition with respect to the useful information at image level. Each image is accordingly different as it is collected during a different time interval.

4.4. SUPPRESSION OF RANDOM FLUCTUATION BY MEANS OF AVERAGE IMAGE CALCULATION.

An average of a number of images, the number of which can be selected, is therefore the best way to suppress noise and to increase contrast.

Noise being chiefly a random value of the picture signal, the sum of a number of images tends to cancel the value of these random fluctuations, this value being further divided by the number of images:

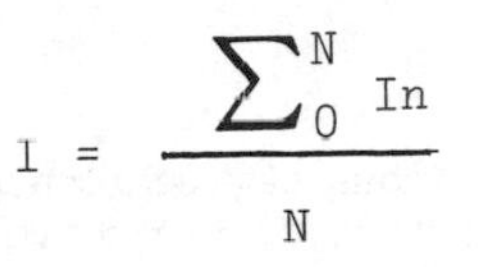

$$I = \frac{\sum_{0}^{N} In}{N}$$

The system used for calculating this average image value offers the choice between 4 and 2048 frames. In the examples chosen to illustrate this, we have used a number of images (N) corresponding to 128 to 256 frames.

5. IMAGE ENHANCEMENT PROCESSING TECHNIQUE

The treatment described above together with those explained below are treatments applied to images which have been digitized. Each image is formatted to a matrix consisting of 520 columns and 576 lines. Each Image point of this matrix may have a value ranging from 0 to 255, i.e. 8 bits. 0 corresponds to black and 255 corresponds to white.

5.1. CONTRAST INCREASE

After noise suppression treatments have been performed, video signal dynamic range is limited as shown in the following figure 4.

A specific function is used in order to reposition the different grey scale values between black (0,3V) and white (1V).

By modifying the brightness level, it is possible to explore the complete grey dynamic range while maintaining an optimal contrast level.

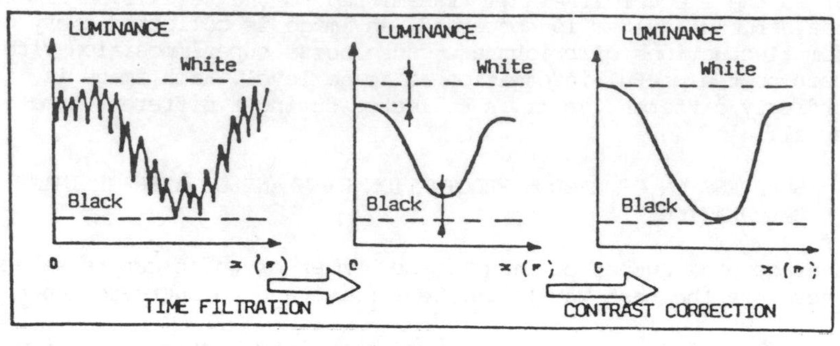

Fig.4.

5.2. SPATIAL FILTRATION

Unsharpness of fluorographic images may be imputed to the size of the X-ray source and also to the nature of the converter screen.

Image unsharpness corresponds to a lack of definition of the contour lines of the object examined and may also cause the loss of smaller image details.

The system used makes it possible to reduce image unsharpness by calculating the value of each image point with respect to adjacent points.
The correction factors may be selected by the operator from 12 menus.

Correction of a number of image points around a certain point may range from 9 to 81.

The greater the geometric distortion of the image, the greater the number of points to be corrected should be selected by the operator.

5.3. SELECTION OF A SPATIAL FILTER

Recognition of an image detail is greatly improved when detail contour lines can easily be identified. The contour of a detail represents a sudden variation of the grey steps. The idea is to boost this grey step variation, using an adequate means.

Filters described above function as shown hereunder:

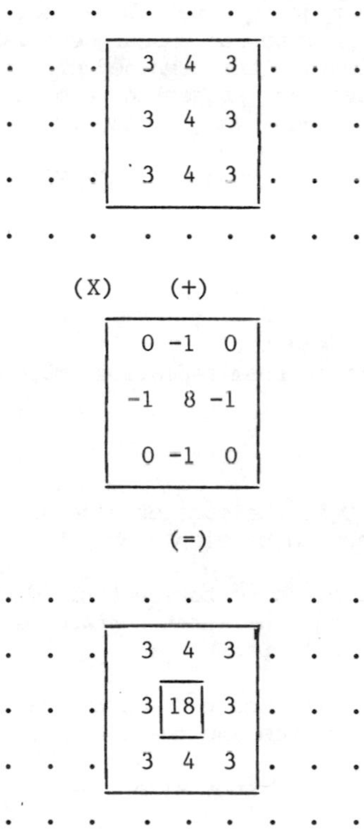

3	4	3
3	4	3
3	4	3

ISOLATED DIGITIZED VALUES OF AN IMAGE

(X) (+)

0	-1	0
-1	8	-1
0	-1	0

EXAMPLE - FILTER N° 1

(=)

3	4	3
3	18	3
3	4	3

RESULT

This filtration is applied in turn to all the image points of the matrix. The electronic circuits used for applying this filtration process are specific and allow fast computation. For instance:

0.5s for a 9 point filter
4 s for an 81 point filter

6. RELATION BETWEEN IMAGE POINT SIZE AND FILTER SELECTION

The useful surface of the detector described above is 220mm in diameter. This image is then formatted in order to form a matrix, through an optical system and the television circuitry. Each element has the following size , 387 x 423micrmetres.

6.1. PERCEPTION OF A SMALL IMAGE DETAIL

On the basis of the two reasons which tend to limit perception of a small detail, i.e. the geometric unsharpness resulting from the size of the radiation source and the detector grain size, the effect of which may be quantified by measuring the internal unsharpness value of the detector, it is possible to calculate the combined effect of both distortions. Several solutions have been suggested: simple addition, root of the sum of squares of these values, etc..

The generally accepted solution is that suggested by "KLASENS" (4):

$$U_t = (U_i^3 + U_g^3)^{\frac{1}{3}}$$

where U_t = total resultant unsharpness
U_i = internal unsharpness of the detector
U_g = geometric unsharpness resulting from radiation source size.

6.2. GEOMETRIC PROJECTION EFFECT (Fig.5).

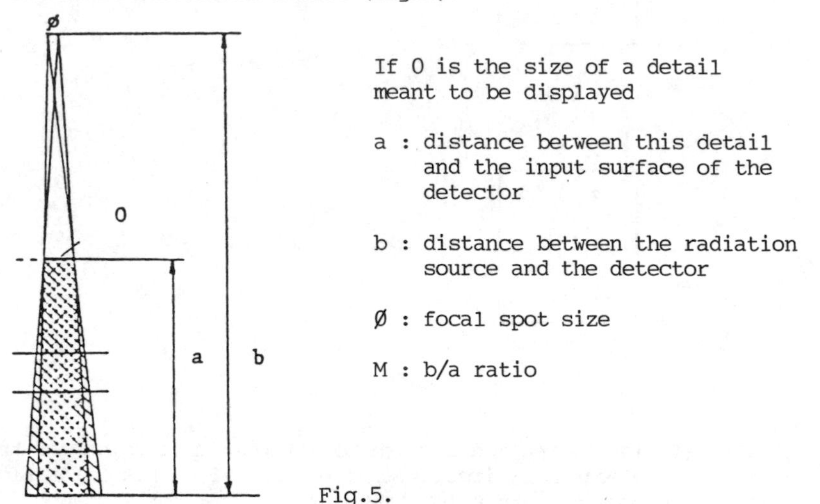

Fig.5.

This small detail will be more perceptible if :

1) it is projected at a larger scale on the detector,

2) the penumbra effect resulting from the size of the radiation source is small with respect to image size.

In other words: $M \times O$ large and $U_g = Ø\,(M - 1)$ $\quad M \times O$

As established by KLASENS the geometric unsharpness U_g is not the only factor responsible for image distortion. Internal unsharpness of the detector should not be disregarded and resultant unsharpness can be expressed as follows:

$$[\ \emptyset\ (M-1)^3 + U_i{}^3\ ]^{\frac{1}{3}}$$

The internal unsharpness value of a fluoroscopic detector is approx. 0.3mm, whereas that of a film used under normal conditions and with an energy radiation under 200kV, is approx. 0.1mm. Assuming a value of 0.3mm and a 0.4mm focal spot diameter, the resultant unsharpness is given in Table 3.

Table 3.

If U_g = (mm)	0,1 U_i	0,5 U_i	U_i	2 U_i	5U_i	10 U_i
U_t (mm)	0.30009	0.3120	0.3779	0.624	1.503	3

When these values are compared with the size of a pixel (0,387 x 0,423)mm, one finds that the resultant unsharpness value corresponds approximately to the size of a pixel of the matrix, when the geometric unsharpness value corresponds to that of the internal unsharpness of the detector.

We have experimentally noted that up to magnification x6, the observer's perception of the image quality indicator wires gradually increases through image magnification.

The following table presents the values of geometric unsharpness and of total resultant unsharpness as a function of different geometric magnification values.

Table 4 also specifies, for each magnification value (M), the number of image points affected by a lack of sharpness.

We have experimentally noted that the best result was in fact achieved by using a filter having an effect on a number of image points corresponding to the global penumbra zone. The examples below demonstrate this statement.

Table 4.

M	2	3	4	5	6
U_g (mm)	0.4	0.8	1.2	1.6	2
U_t (mm)	0.449	0.813	1.206	1.603	200
number of image points	2	2	3	4	5

7. RESULTS

The two diagrams, Figs.6,7 show the increase of radiographic sensitivity that can be achieved by means of an image enhancement system.

The system we have used and which offers such capabilities is the Quantel "CRYSTAL" system.

8. APPLICATIONS

The following examples (Figs.8 - 12) show what quality difference can be achieved in the industrial fields of steel welding, metal casting and manufacture of arms.

9. CONCLUSIONS

I wish to end this paper by insisting on the extremely high inter-dependence of all the radiological parameters which lead to better results in the field of fluoroscopic examinations. One should also bear in mind that these factors may sometimes influence results in the opposite direction expected.

For example, when preference is given to geometric magnification in order to increase perception or display of small details, the detector radiation level decreases, so that the energy level has to be increased to achieve the same penetration value.

A large photon flux is preferable in order to increase image contrast, but also requires a larger emissive surface, so that geometric unsharpness increases.

It is therefore difficult to define a general rule and a specific procedure for all applications in the field of fluoroscopy.
In fact, a compromise is often the only solution to the problem.

10. PUBLICATIONS

(1) Standard Guide for Radiologic Real-Time Imaging
ASTM DESIGNATION E.1000-84

(2) X-Ray Real-Time Imaging for Weld Inspection - IIW Progress Report.
British Journal of NDT, March 1986 pp. 89 - 92

(3) A,ROSE, Vision, Human and Electronic,
Plenum Press New York 1973

(4) H.A.KLASENS "Measurement and Calculations of Unsharpness Combination in X-Ray Photography".
Philips Research Reports Vol.1, no.4, August 1946, pp.241 - 249.

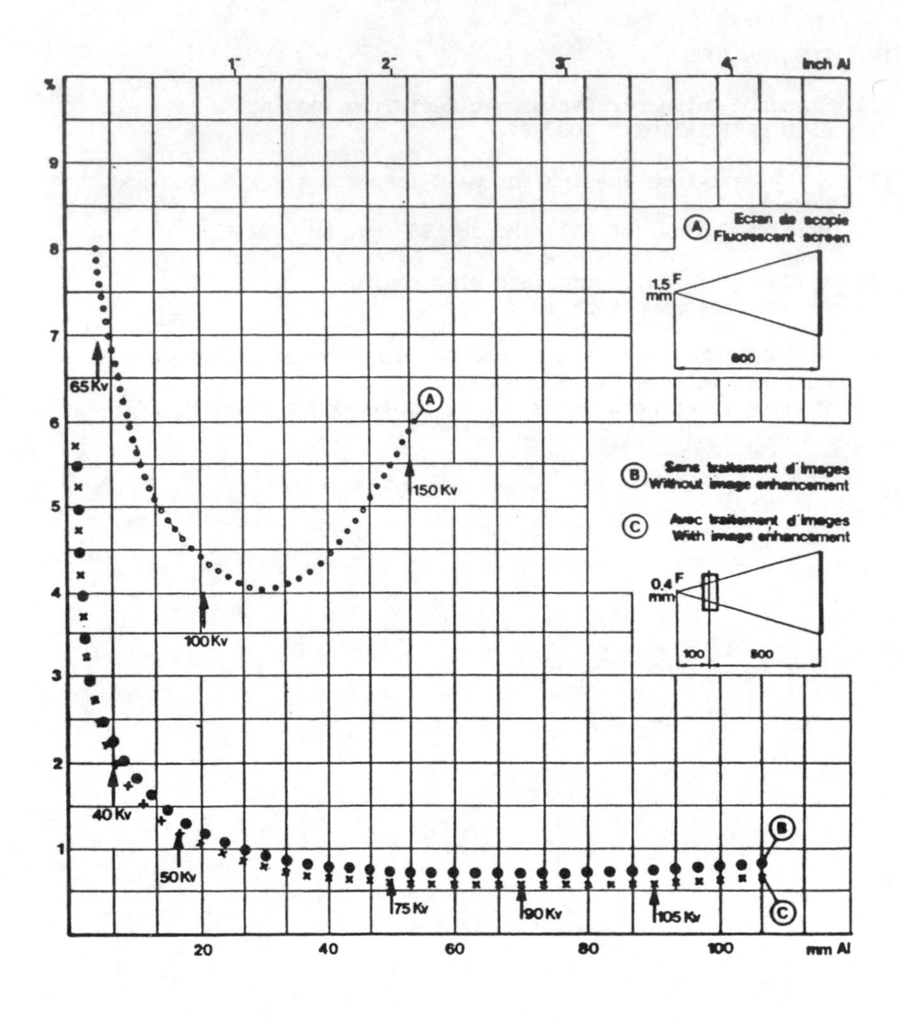

Sensibilité IQI à fils. Objet immobile
Wire IQI sensitivity. Motionless object
Al 30-150Kv

Fig 6

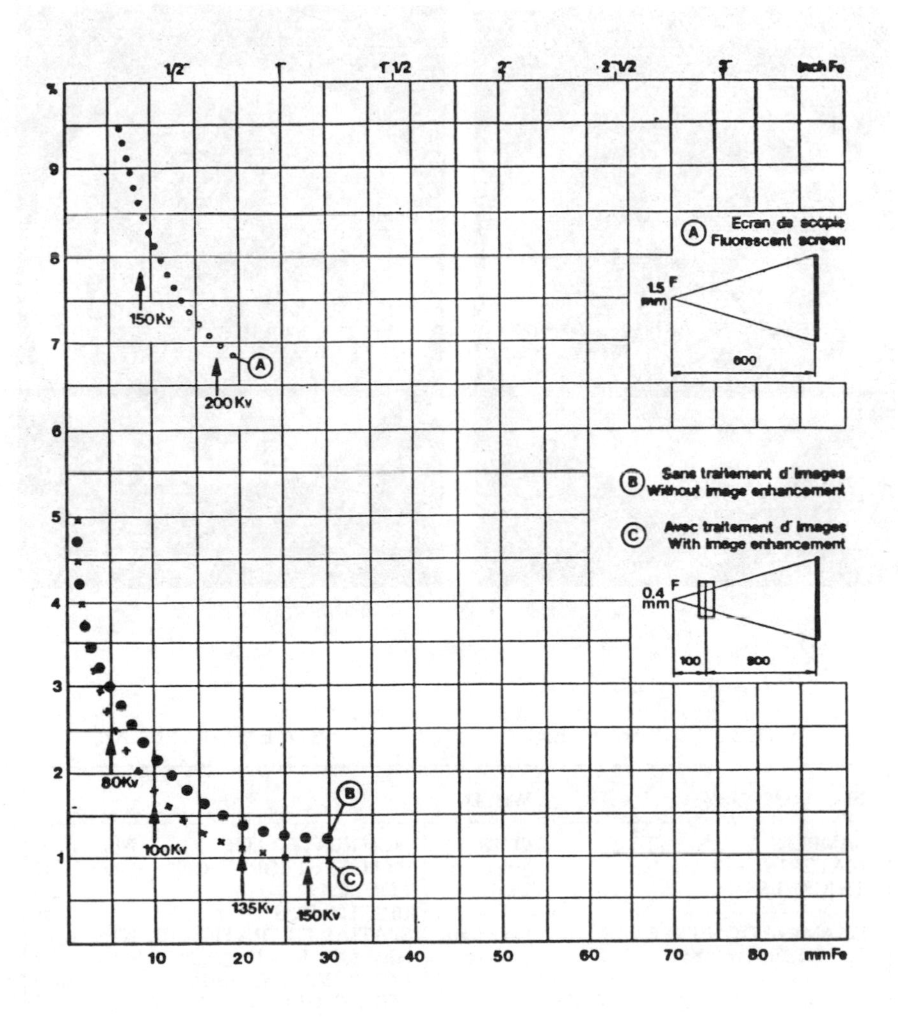

Sensibilité IQI à fils. Objet immobile
Wire IQI sensitivity. Motionless object — Fe 90-400 Kv

Fig 7

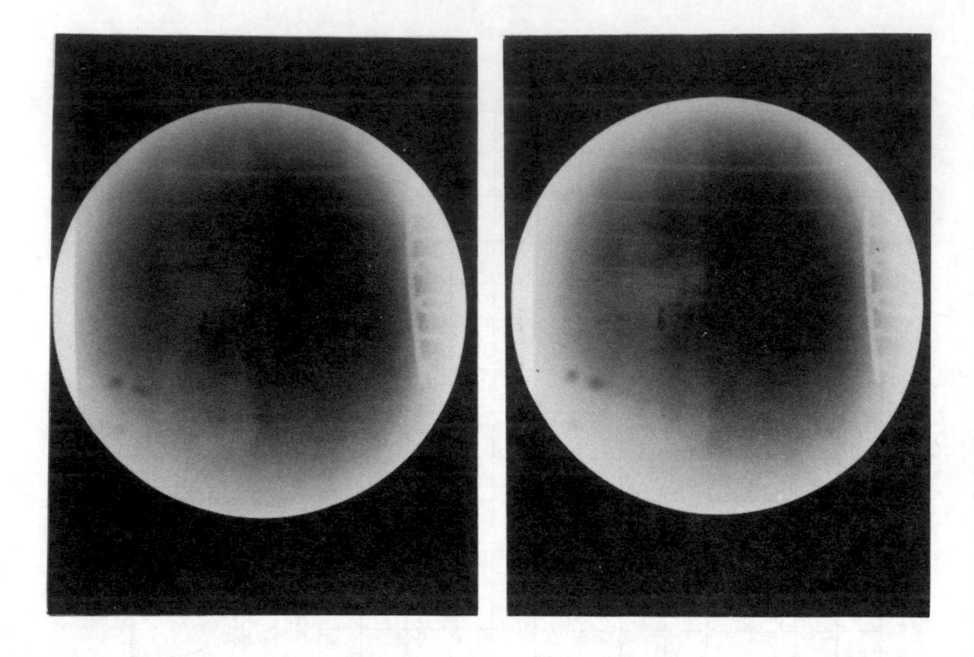

WITHOUT ENHANCEMENT | WITH ENHANCEMENT

FLUOROSCOPY		WELD			
SAMPLE	Tube	Ø 108	IMAGE AVERAGE	Nbre	0
MATERIAL		Steel	IMAGE INTEGRATION	Nbre	128
THICKNESS		2 x 6	CONTRAST	%	122
			BRIGHTNESS		95
EXAMINATION TYPE		Dble wall	SPATIAL FILTRATION	N°	2
FAULT/FLAW TYPE		porosity	REF. MEASURE		0
			COMP. WITH ST. REF.		0
EXAMINATION PARAMETERS			THRESHOLD		0
	kV	118			
	mA	3	NOTE		
FOCAL SPOT - SCREEN DIST		500	CONCLUSIONS		
GEOMETRIC MAGNIFICATION		4	Visible 6° wire		
FILTRATION		0	Fault sharpness		
MASKING		0	Sharpness increase of fault		
ELECT. MAGNIFICATION		0	contour lines		

Fig 8

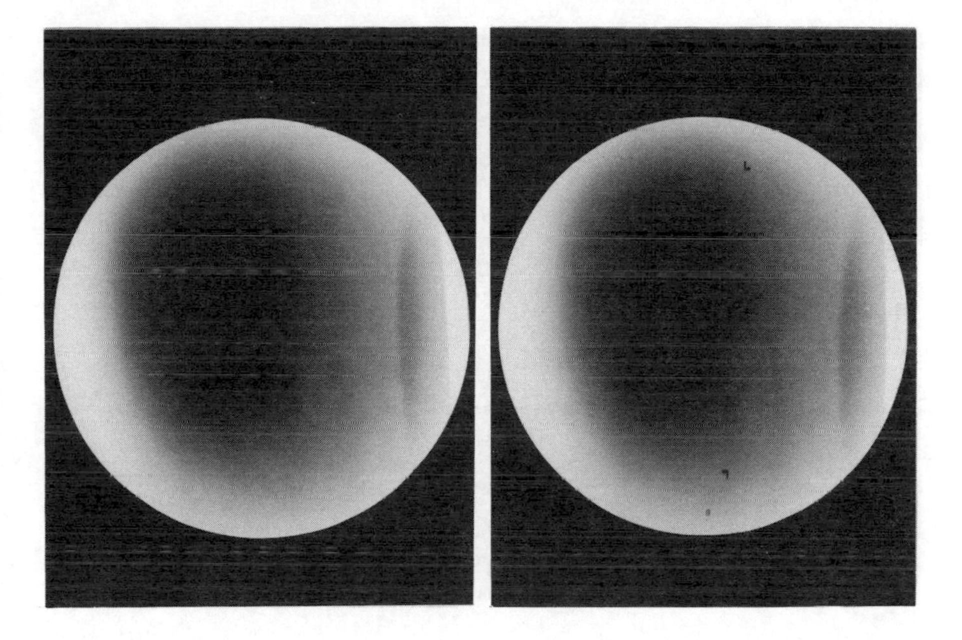

WITHOUT ENHANCEMENT			WITH ENHANCEMENT		
FLUOROSCOPY		SHELL			
SAMPLE	Type	2" .75	IMAGE AVERAGE	Nbr	0
MATERIAL	Steel	2x6mm Fe	IMAGE INTEGRATION	Nbr	128
THICKNESS	Explosive	57.85	CONTRAST	%	122
			BRIGHTNESS		95
EXAMINATION TYPE		Rotation	SPATIAL FILTRATION	N°	2
FAULT/FLAW TYPE		cracks	REF. MEASURE		0
			COMP. WITH ST. REF.		0
EXAMINATION PARAMETERS			THRESHOLD		0
	kV	118			
	mA	3	NOTE:		
FOCAL SPOT - SCREEN DIST		500	Object rotation absolutely		
GEOMETRIC MAGNIFICATION		4	necessary		
FILTRATION		0	CONCLUSIONS		
MASKING		0	Visible cracks through two steel walls		
ELECT. MAGNIFICATION		0			

Fig 9

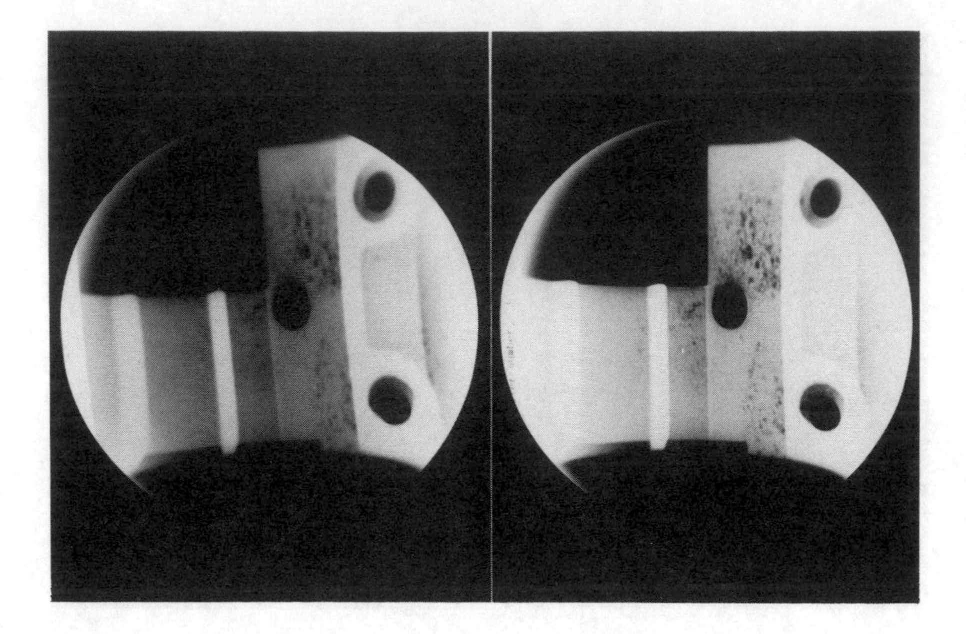

WITHOUT ENHANCEMENT | WITH ENHANCEMENT

FLUOROSCOPY				
SAMPLE		IMAGE AVERAGE	Nbr	0
MATERIAL	Aluminium	IMAGE INTEGRATION	Nbr	128
THICKNESS mm	4-15	CONTRAST	%	100
		BRIGHTNESS		100
EXAMINATION TYPE	Rotation	SPATIAL FILTRATION	N°	3
FAULT/FLAW TYPE	Micropor	REF. MEASURE		0
		COMP. WITH ST. REF.		0
EXAMINATION PARAMETERS		THRESHOLD		0
kV	40			
mA	3	NOTE:		
FOCAL SPOT - SCREEN DIST	600			
GEOMETRIC MAGNIFICATION	4			
FILTRATION	0	CONCLUSIONS		
MASKING	0			
ELECT. MAGNIFICATION	0			

Fig 10

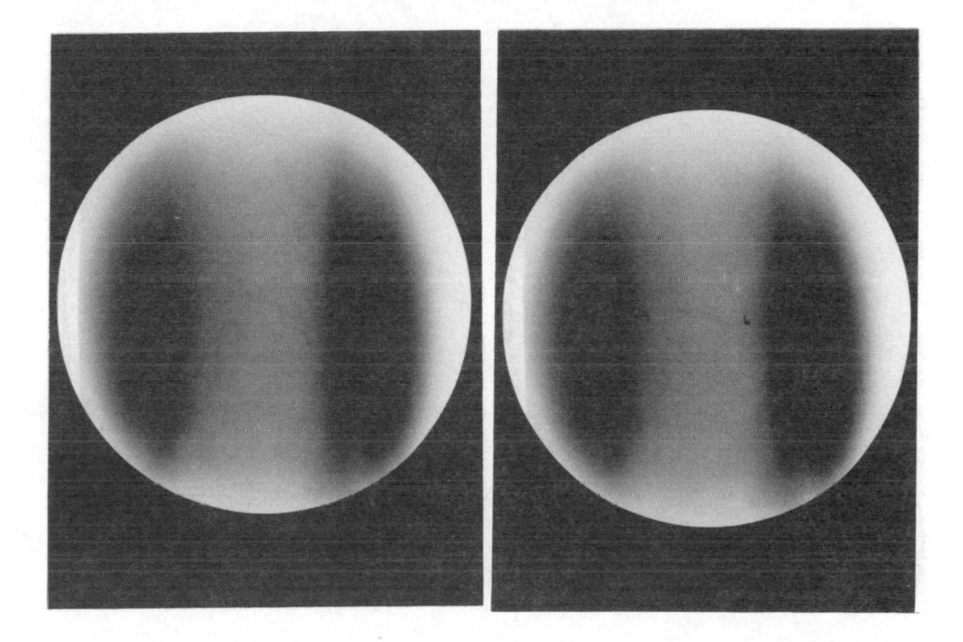

WITHOUT ENHANCEMENT

FLUOROSCOPY		
SAMPLE		Butt weld
MATERIAL		Steel
THICKNESS	Bead	18
EXAMINATION TYPE cont.		product
FAULT/FLAW TYPE		Cracks
EXAMINATION PARAMETERS		
	kV	126
	mA	3
FOCAL SPOT - SCREEN DIST		600
GEOMETRIC MAGNIFICATION		5
FILTRATION		0
MASKING		collim on tube
ELECT. MAGNIFICATION		2

WITH ENHANCEMENT

IMAGE AVERAGE	Nbr	0
IMAGE INTEGRATION	Nbr	128
CONTRAST	%	100
BRIGHTNESS		100
SPATIAL FILTRATION	N°	10
REF. MEASURE		0
COMP. WITH ST. REF.		0
THRESHOLD		0

NOTE:

CONCLUSIONS: Increased sharpness of crack shape and importance

Fig 11

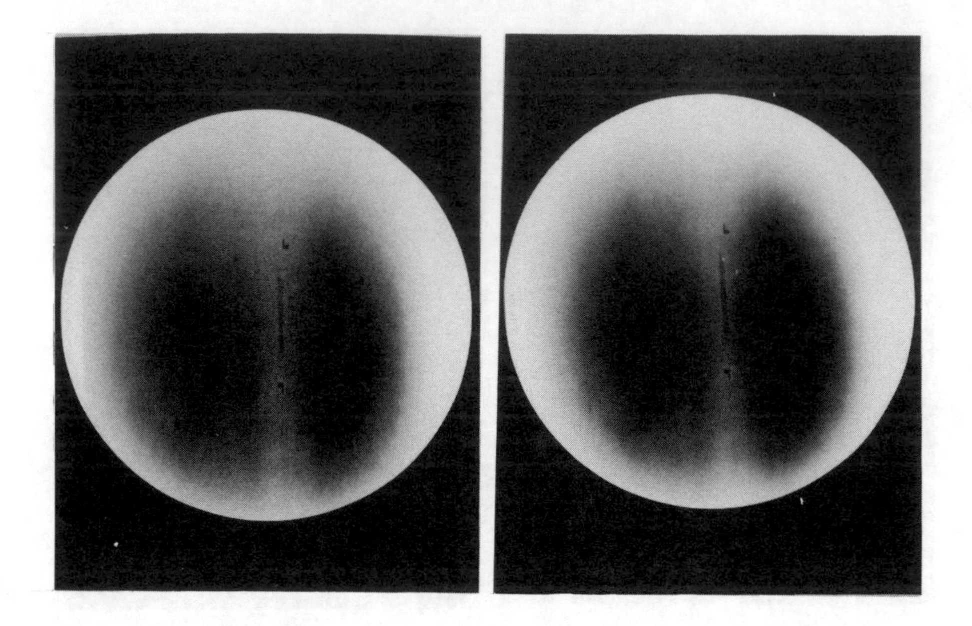

WITHOUT ENHANCEMENT | WITH ENHANCEMENT

FLUOROSCOPY	WELD		
SAMPLE Tube MATERIAL Steel THICKNESS	Ø 125 Stainless 2 x 10	IMAGE AVERAGE Nbr IMAGE INTEGRATION Nbr CONTRAST % BRIGHTNESS SPATIAL FILTRATION N° REF. MEASURE COMP. WITH ST. REF. THRESHOLD	0 64 116 92 4
EXAMINATION TYPE FAULT/FLAW TYPE bad	Dble wall Penetr.		
EXAMINATION PARAMETERS kV mA FOCAL SPOT - SCREEN DIST GEOMETRIC MAGNIFICATION FILTRATION MASKING ELECT. MAGNIFICATION	Continu 160 3 4 0 0 0 0	NOTE: Accurate definition of limits of insufficient penetration CONCLUSIONS	

Fig 12

FULLY AUTOMATED X-RAY INSPECTION

Dr W ROYE, A KRAUSE

Automated image processing, e.g. image interpreation and defect evaluation, yields a higher reliability than any human inspector. However, it will be suggested that there is never a chance of achieving 100% reliability. Other aspects, as for example, the flexibility and inspection speed will be discussed. Flexibility is of great importance, to cover object design changes, and the inspection speed must always be considered in a case of integrating the inspection system into a manufacturing process. There is a broad spectrum of applications for fully automated X-ray inspection. Two examples are presented in this paper.

INTRODUCTION

Due to increasing automation and tightening up of manufacturer's liability, and especially also in the case of inspection of objects which are relevant concerning safety, X-ray inspection systems must be implemented into CIM-concepts.
Like other disciplines, the X-ray inspection technique changes from manual work being combined with visual X-ray image interpretation over certain automated individual solutions to inspection systems, which are completely integrated into a computer-controlled manufacturing process. Thus, new pre-requisites have to be considered, being quite different to those in combination with conventional visual image interpretation.

The pre-requisites for a fully automated X-ray system are:

Philips GmbH, SC Industrial X-ray, Rontgenstrasse 24-26
D-2000 Hamburg 63. FRG.

- highest inspection reliability
- high inspection speed
- flexibility of the inspection system.

Therefore the requirements concerning the X-ray technique itself as well as the imaging system also increase.

Short and long-term stability, high signal-to-noise ratios, highest reproducibility, are only some of these new requirements.
In this article the special problems which occur during the development of fully automated X-ray systems will be pointed out and discussed.

INSPECTION RELIABILITY

An increasing quality conscience and the problems around the manufacturer's liability demand increasingly higher inspection reliability. Before discussing this aspect, the inspection reliability has to be defined as follows:

- the inspection reliability, being expressed as a percentage (%),is the relation between the inspection results and the true facts.

There are two types of false inspection results:

- Objects without defects are rejected (false alarm rate).
- Objects with defects are not rejected (defect detection probability).

While the defect detection probability represents a safety problem, the false alarm rate reduces production capacity and increases production costs.

The two methods to measure the inspection reliability are:

- comparison of computer results with the results of visual inspection, considering a quantity of objects or defects;
- evaluating the reliability, using artificial flaws e.g. drilled holes.

The first method has the disadvantage that the quality of an objective method (computer) is evaluated by a subjective one (human inspector). To reduce this problem, it may be possible to use a mean value of various human inspection results. A further improvement is given when a collection of objects with all possible defect types, defect sizes, defect orientations and defect positions is achievable.

The second method, which uses artificial defects, implies much less effort and it yields high reproducibility; however, it does not give any idea of the detection probability or false alarm rate of real defects, due to their different properties. Therefore, this method seems only to be suited to evaluate the general functionality of an inspection system.

There are qualitative and quantitative differences when comparing computer and human reliability:
The reliability of a human inspector is influenced by many subjective factors, e.g. weariness, inattention, wrong evaluation of defects near the registration level and others. These factors may lead sometimes to catastrophic results; for example, Trumpfheller (ref.1) once pointed out that after a NDT inspection of an 800metre long weld by three different inspectors, a correspondence of only 33% of the three results was achieved !
Another test gave a maximum inspection reliability for the X-ray weld inspection of 70% !
On the other hand, both the detection probability and the false alarm rate given by computer image interpretation are of a systematic nature. Wrong interpretations are reproducible and are always based on certain reasons -

- insufficient contrast
- non-optimised algorithms
- undefined defect types and sizes
- non-optimised inspection positions.

Therefore, it is possible to improve the reliability; however, there is a relationship between reliability and effort - Fig.1.

The effort implies the mechanical handling system, the computer system, and the resulting inspection speed.
The diagram demonstrates that due to the asymptotic behaviour of the relationship, a 100% reliability will never be achievable, but, based on the results of statistical measurements we are able to point out that the reliability being achieved by a computer is already higher than that of visual inspection. Because of the systematic nature of computer results on the one hand, and because of technical progress concerning the development of algorithms on the other hand, a further improvement can be expected.

FLEXIBILITY
The implementation of automated image processing is especially efficient in the case of the inspection of large quantities of the same object. But even in this case, sometimes new object types are accepted into the production programme, sometimes changes in object design and sometimes only detail changes - e.g. object identification or tolerance changes have to be included. In such

cases our customers ask for flexible systems, which means that a new programming should not be necessary, or at least, should be as easy and simple as possible. But this requires for complex tasks, intelligent algorithms being combined with corresponding computer capacities. A compromise is given by an interactive menu-controlled change of defined parameters.

CLASSIFICATION OF INSPECTION TASKS

The inspection tasks can be divided into three different groups with different grades of difficulty:-

- interactive measurement of known shapes
- detection and measurement of objects which are known or which can easily be separated from the background
- detection and measurement of defects with unknown shapes and positions on a complex background.

In the following two examples of industrial projects, representatives of the second and third groups will be demonstrated.

FULLY AUTOMATED X-RAY INSPECTION OF MULTILAYER PCB's

An example of the second group is the Philips system MU90S which was designed for the inspection of multilayer printed circuit boards. The special task is to find out whether there is a displacement between the different layers, and in the case of a displacement, it has to be measured. These values will then serve as correcting parameters for the further production process.
For this purpose, concentric rings of copper with different diameters are provided on each layer, thus enabling a measurement of the concentricity of these by means of a vertical projection with X-rays.
Figure 2 is a photograph of the X-ray cabinet MU90S and Fig.3 represents an X-ray image of such a concentric marker system.

The whole system requires:-

- a 160kV X-ray equipment using an X-ray tube with a 0.4mm focal spot size
- a searchray TV camera, target size 9 x 12mm
- an X-Y table to shift the pc board
- an image processing computer.

To enable a measurement in different areas of the board and to enable a measurement of up to 24 layers, a lot of marker systems, each with a diameter of 6mm are provided.

The automatic inspection works as follows:-

- The X-Y table shifts the PCB into preselected positions.
- The corresponding X-ray parameters are set by computer programme
- The X-ray image is converted into a video signal by the searchray camera
- The image processing computer digitizes the video signal into an image of 512 x 512 pixels.
- To reduce the noise, an integration over several frames is performed.
- In some cases a shading correction is necessary
- Adaptive discrimination is used for segmentation
- Evaluation of the concentricity of the discriminated objects with an accuracy of ±25μm. The differences of the "centres of gravity" of the individual rings of the marker system represent the displacement of the layers.
- Considering preset displacement tolerances, the inspected PCBs are sorted into three categories:-
    - displacement is acceptable
    - displacement is not acceptable, but can be corrected by the drilling machine
    - displacement is not acceptable and correction is not possible.

The MU90S inspection system is designed for manual loading, thus representing an off-line system, as well as for automatic handling, e.g. using a robot, when the inspection will be carried out in-line, being integrated into a production process.

AUTOMATED WHEEL INSPECTION SYSTEM

In November 1987 Philips installed its first fully automated aluminium-alloy wheel inspection system in the factory of a well-known automobile manufacturer. The system enables the inspection of cast aluminium wheels corresponding to actual specifications. The inspection implies the detection and measurement of defects, for example, porosity, shrinkage cavities and segregations.

The equipment consists of the following components:-

- X-ray cabinet with a five-axis manipulator
- Highly stabilised constant potential X-ray set MG-164 with small focus X-ray tube
- Image intensifier with TV chain
- Conveyor belt for the transport of the wheels
- Switch cabinet with the computer for numerical control
- Image processing computer
- The operator's desk

Every inspection cycle contains the following steps:-

- Height measurement: the wheel is transported by the conveyor belt to a device which measures its height. This value is needed for the specially designed manipulator, which handles the wheel in programmed positions between the X-ray tube and the image intensifier.
- Wheel type recognition: for this purpose the first X-ray image is used.
- Integration: to improve the signal-to-noise ratio, an integration over several television frames is necessary.
- Object handling: due to object design and geometrical dimensions and because of the limited diameter of the image intensifier, a lot of different positions have to be provided - actually, 80 positions.
- To achieve both data reduction and speed, 16 images are compiled into a 512 x 512 matrix and then processed.
- The first steps of preprocessing are the shading correction and a contrast enhancement.
- A bandpass filtering follows, where the selection of the filter matrix depends on contrast and brightness distribution.
- The segmentation: the most complicated and time-consuming step is the discrimination of defects, the unequivocal differentiation between geometrical indications (edges, holes, numbers) and relevant defect indications. Areas of different brightness require different segmentation parameters. A suitable way is given by means of erosion and dilatation algorithms or by measuring geometrical properties. It is important that these algorithms do not require fixed masks, but are calculated dynamically for all actual images.
- Measurement and decision: all defects are measured under object- and area-specific aspects. Object-specific parameters are the diameter, the area, the perimeter and an area-specific parameter is the density of defects, e.g. the number of defects in a defined area. Taking now the actual specification into account, this classification of defects is the base for the decision, whether the inspected object has to be accepted or rejected.

RESULTS OF STATISTICAL TESTS

After the optimisation of the algorithms, a statistical test was carried out. For this purpose 100 wheels with typical natural defects were used. The inspection was performed three times with different positions, thus representing an inspection test of 300 wheels. All the wheels had not yet been machined and not been previously inspected.

Using a comparison of the computer decision with human decision, the results of the test were as follows:

- 97% of the decisions were correct.
- The false alarm rate was found to be 1%.
- The rate of undetected relevant defects was 2%

These undetected defects were unknown until this test and therefore not considered in the discrimination algorithms.

The practical work with the automated X-ray system leads the attention to the necessity of flexible algorithms, due to the following aspects:-

- slight changes of wheel design
- differences between different moulds
- change in the grade of abrasive
- height of type of marks.

These changes may lead, if they are not considered, to bad results concerning defect detection probability and/or false alarm rate.

The time which today is required for the automated inspection of one individual wheel is of the order of 6 minutes, including height measurement, type recognition, handling and complete image processing.
For comparison, the human operator needs, for the same task between 60 and 90 seconds.
Six minutes is the inspection time of the prototype system which was optimised firstly under the aspects of reliability and flexibility but not yet under the aspect of the inspection speed.
Further development work therefore will be dedicated to the improvement of inspection speed, aiming at an inspection time which corresponds to that of visual inspection.

CONCLUSION

The report gives an overview over Philips fully-automated X-ray systems. High inspction reliability, high inspection speed and flexibility are the requirements.

The reliability which was achieved was found to be much higher than that of any visual inspection method.

The software flexibility has also reached a relative high level. However, the inspection speed does not yet match that of visual inspection, and under this aspect still a lot of further development has to be carried out.

REFERENCES

1. Trumpfeller R.
Zuverlassigkeit der zerstorungsfreien Prufung. 4th Int. Konf. Zerstorungsfreie Prufung in der Kerntechnik. May 1981 Lindau. S 247-261.

2. Fischdick H, Herman K.
Auffindbarkeit von systematischen Querrissen in Schweissnahten bei der Ultraschallprufung nach deutschen Regelwerken.
Jahrstagung DGZfP, Mai 1987, Lindau S.371-383.

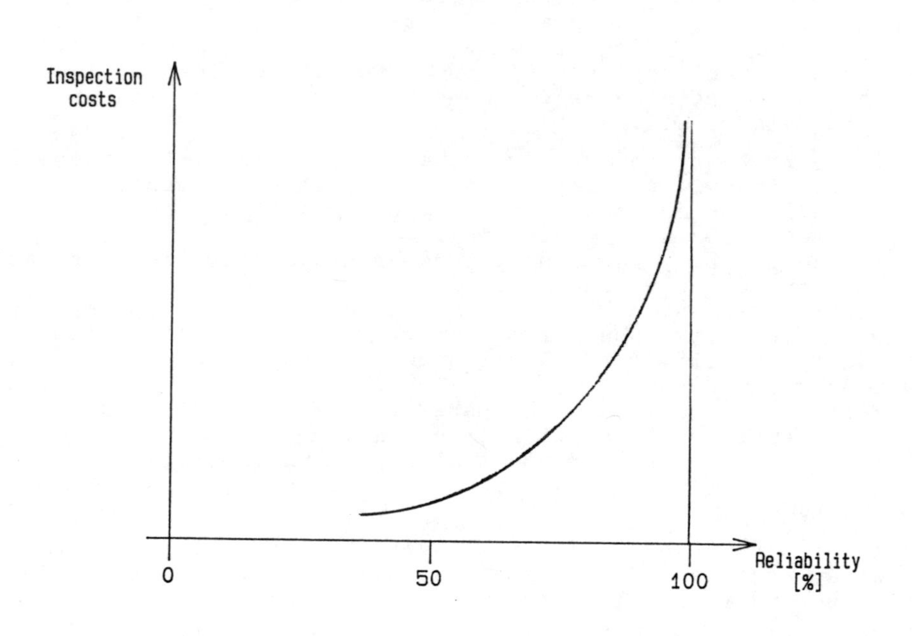

Fig.1. The relation between inspection reliability and effort.

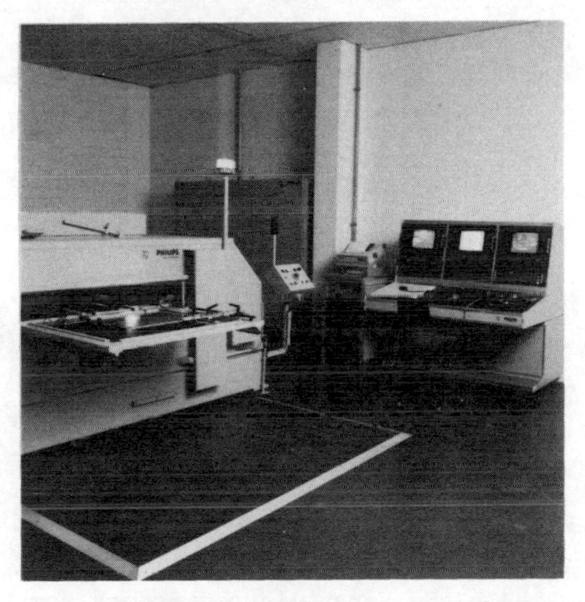

Fig. 2: X-ray system MU90S for the inspection of multilayer boards.

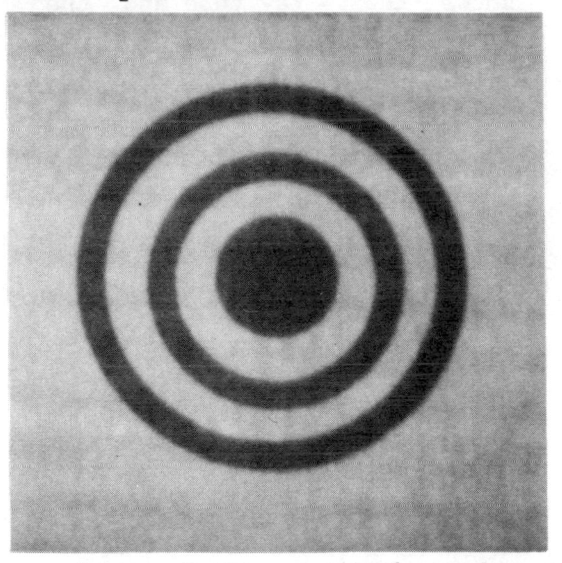

Fig. 3: X-ray image of the concentric marker system

Fig. 4: PHILIPS X-ray inspection system MU31F for automatic wheel inspection. The photograph shows the X-ray tube and the manipulator with the object

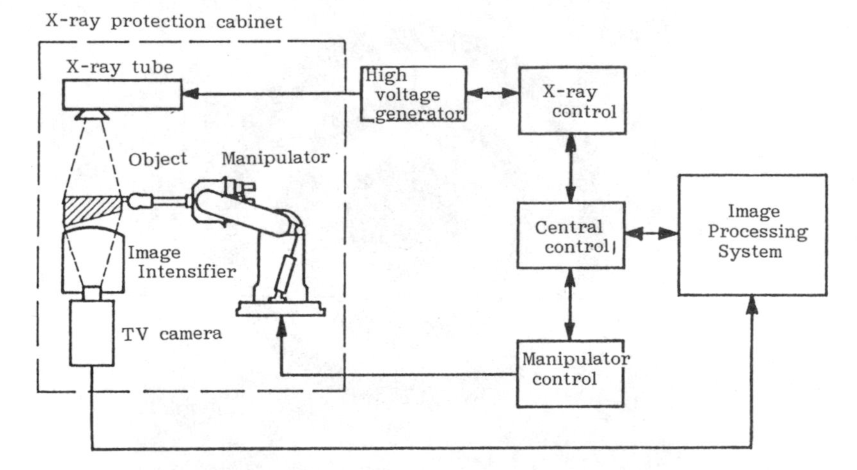

Fig.5. Schematic of the automated X-ray inspection system.

AUTOMATIC EVALUATION OF WELD RADIOGRAPHS BY DIGITAL IMAGE PROCESSING

J.H. BUILTJES, P. ROSE AND W. DAUM

Real-time image analysis in X-ray inspection of welds is a complex field of pattern recognition. The aim of computerized inspection is the automatic flaw classification. In this article each step of image processing necessary for this purpose is described and discussed. By means of X-ray images of welds it is demonstrated how the real-time evaluation can be realized successfully.

INTRODUCTION

Digital image processing becomes an important tool for the evaluation of X-ray images in industrial radiography. Today, most of the X-ray real-time systems are supplied with special equipments to enhance the images for a better visual inspection. Procedures such as averaging and filtering increase the signal-to-noise ratio and improve the displayed image. The interpretation of the image contents, however, is still done by the human observer. The problem of automatic inspection exists in detection and classification of defects and requires high sophisticated image analysis methods. For the evaluation of weld radiographs, this paper presents new investigations about flaw characterization by the use of digital image processing.

The flow chart in figure 1 shows the image processing steps necessary for computerized inspection. The image preprocessing has the function of emphasizing the defect

Dipl.-Ing. J.H. Builtjes, Dipl.-Ing. P. Rose, Dipl.-Ing. W.Daum, Federal Institute for Materials Research and Testing (BAM), Berlin

indications in the image. The recognition of the weld defects is realized by a special segmentation algorithm and will be described below. For the characterization of the weld defects, different operations of feature extraction will be discussed. Several features, tested on real defects, were evaluated by statistical methods. The most significant features were stored in a digital data base to supervise the final flaw classification. The following chapters correspond to the sequential processing steps in figure 1.

PREPROCESSING

For visual inspection, the aim of preprocessing is to improve the readability of radiographs for the human observer. A lot of operations such as contrast enhancement, shading correction, pseudo-color-transformation etc. are available and most of them can be executed in real-time even by low-cost image-processing systems. For automatic inspection, however, the purpose of preprocessing is to build up a good image for the flaw detection algorithm. In this case much more complex operations, especially for the noise reduction, are necessary.

The easiest and most effective method is image integration or superposition. A number of images, i. e. frames from a TV-camera, are summed and averaged. The success of this procedure depends on the depth of the summing memory, which should be 16 bit for an 8 bit digitization, and on the number of superposed images.

Another method to reduce noise is digital filtering. With the help of digital processing it is possible to filter images in two different ways:

- Filtering in the frequency domain
- Filtering in the spatial domain

Digital filtering in the frequency domain gives a higher degree of flexibility than filtering in the spatial domain. The images are first transformed to the frequency domain and then multiplied by the filter function. This function can be adapted to the image contents, i. e. direction of cracks and weld seam or frequency components of the image.

Because the Fourier-Transformation needs a lot of computation-time, this filtering method isn't suitable for real-time applications.

Digital filtering in the spatial domain can be executed by using hardware components. Hence, it is used very often for real-time image processing. In Fig. 2 three different digital filters are presented. All three filters can produce a good noise reduction. The edge and peak in tne original image are influenced by the different filter methods in different ways. The filters are having the following properties.

- Low pass filter (mean value calculation of nearest neighbours). This filtering generates a loss of spatial resolution. The edge is spread out and the peak is smoothed.
- Median filter (median calculation of nearest neighbours). The edge remains sharp, but the peak is suppressed completely.
- Sigma filter (mean value calculation of nearest neighbours depending on the local greylevel distribution). Without smoothing the edge and peak this filter reaches the same noise reduction as the low pass filter.

DEFECT DETECTION

The following summary shows which difficulties result from image structures of a weld radiograph for the automatic defect recognition:

defect position - In one part of a weld multiple defects can occur at the same place and the images can superimpose upon each other.

defect types - The big number of different weld defects and their varying representation in the radiograph prevent a direct search with pre-defined references.

defect contrast - Defect recognition methods are based on the detection of local density differences. A reliable defect detection can only be guaranteed if the image input system (e.g. TV-camera) registers the local contrast sufficiently.

image structure - Radiographs of normal welds include some image structures (e.g. irregularities of the weld surface and shape, reinforcement) which may look like imperfections. These can cause mis-interpretation by the image analysis procedure.

Fig. 3 shows a flow chart of the automatic detection of weld defects. The main part of the algorithm is the defect segmentation procedure. With the aid of an analytical description of the two-dimensional image function, a so-called background model is computed and subtracted from the original image. After image subtraction, weld defects can simply be isolated by different well-known image processing operations and an object correlation method. The result of the image analysis procedure is a binary image which is shown in Fig. 5, the corresponding original X-ray image is shown in Fig. 4. The whole algorithm works automatically, without any interactive communication with an operator.

FEATURE EXTRACTION

In order to be able to classify the different defects found by the segmentation algorithm, a number of defect characteristics has to be calculated. From the theory of pattern recognition the followig characteristics should be the most powerful to describe different defects.

C_1 convex contour length/contour length
C_2 area/convex area
C_3 minimal extent/maximal extent
C_4 convex minimal extent/convex maximal extent
C_5 formfactor
C_6 convex formfactor

For all the characteristics C_i listed above we can write: $0 \leq C_i \leq 1$. The formfactor F is defined as:

$$F = \frac{4 \pi A}{L^2}$$

with A the area, and L the contour length of the defect presentation. The convex formfactor is calculated by using the convex area and the convex contour length. The formfactor defined here is based on the shape of a circle. For a circle $F = 1$; for an infinite thin and infinite long line $F = 0$. The usefulness of the characteristics mentioned above for defect classification can be tested with the aid of a data base for weld flaws.

DIGITAL IMAGE DATA BASE

An image data base for weld flaws was configurated and filled with about 200 images and about 2000 flaws. Generally an image data base for flaws in radiographs contains the following main items:

- Digitized original recording, defect types arranged
- Detailed descriptions of the specimen and of the manufacture conditions
- Description of the recording system (image intensifier, camera, image preprocessing)
- Quantitative information about defect characteristics
- Results of manifold visual defect classification

For the automatic flaw classification the two last items are the most important. For our study the following properties are of great interest:

1. Weld flaws are divided in several well known classes like e.g. cracks, gasholes and solid inclusions,
2. with the different defect characteristics a multidimensional feature space can be built.

The combination of the calculated defect characteristics and the information of the visual defect classification makes it possible to define so-called separation functions. Because of the great number of stored defects in the data base this can be done with good statistical reliability. The automatic defect classification is based on these separation functions.

From the data base the distributions of the defect characteristics can be obtained. The usefulness of the different characteristics can be determined by studying these distribution curves.

The possibility to separate two distributions curves representing two flaw classes can be described by means of a quality factor Q:

$$Q = \frac{(m_1 - m_2)^2}{s_1^2 + s_2^2} \qquad , 0 < Q < \infty$$

with m_1,m_2 the mean values of the two distributions curves and s_1, s_2 the two standard deviations. In Fig. 6 two possible configurations of curves are shown. For the configuration in Fig. 6a, Q will be much greater than for the configuration in Fig. 6b.

Fig. 7 and Fig. 8 are showing some typical distributions of real defects. For Fig. 7,Q = 36.0 and for Fig. 8

Q = 0.4. After having calculated the quality factor Q for all possible distribution combinations, it is possible to determine by using these quality factors the best characteristics (that means those characterstics which separate the different defect types in the best possible manner), and define the separation functions for the defect classification.

FLAW CLASSIFICATION

The separation functions are dividing the characteristic space into subspaces which are representing the defect classes. Hence, by using the database, classification is reduced to a sorting procedure in predefined classes. Nevertheless, for each defect detected by the segmentation algorithm, all the features characterizing the flaw types must be calculated. However, for special applications it is possible to reduce the number of defect classes and defect characteristics. In other words, every application has its own typical set of separation functions. Fig. 10 shows the result of a classification using the four defect classes: cracks, gasholes, solid inclusions and lack of penetration. In this example the separation functions were user-defined and optimized for this image contents. The success of the classification can be demonstrated by comparing the original X-ray radiograph in Fig. 9 with the result in Fig. 10.

CONCLUSION

The image processing strategy described in this paper is a successful method for flaw classification. For an automatic inspection system the image processing steps mentioned above should be executed in real-time. Therefore the followig operations must be available as hardware components: image integration, digital filtering, image combining (subtraction), threshold operations, parameter calculations for binary objects. Most of these operations are available in commercial image processing systems.

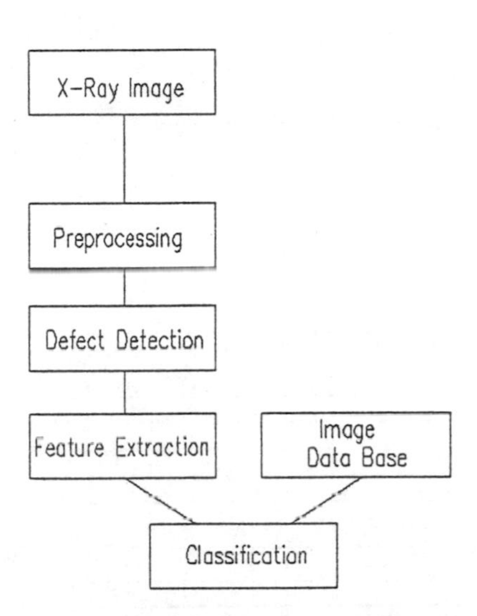

Fig. 1 Flow chart of the automatic weld defect classification

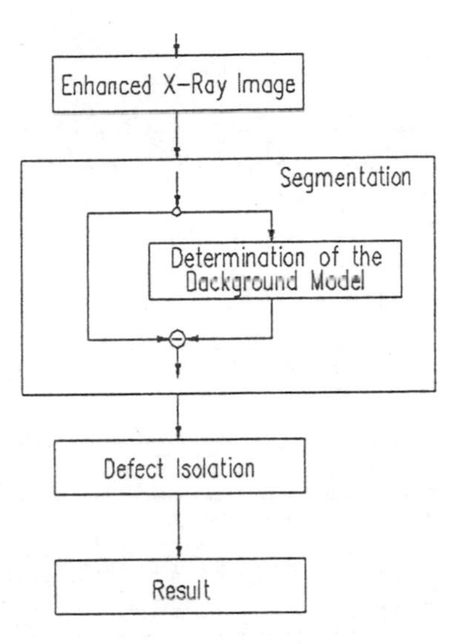

Fig. 3 Flow chart of the segmentation algorithm

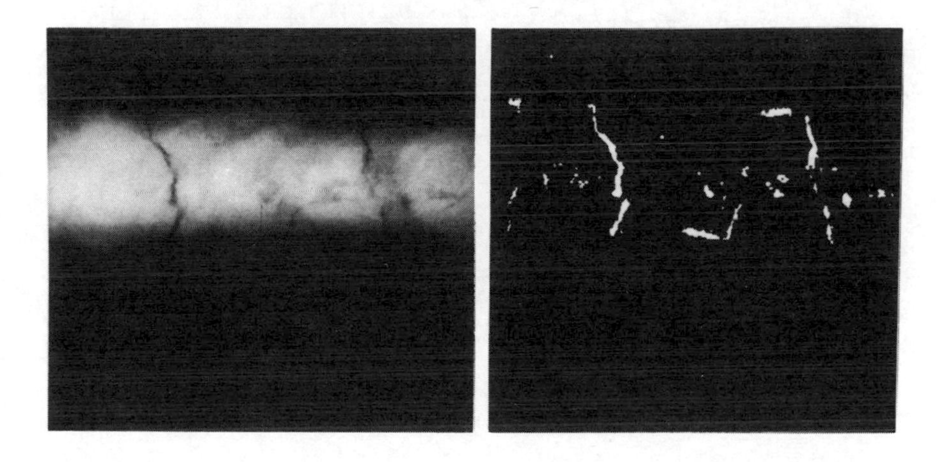

Fig. 4 Weld radiograph

Fig. 5 Segmentation result

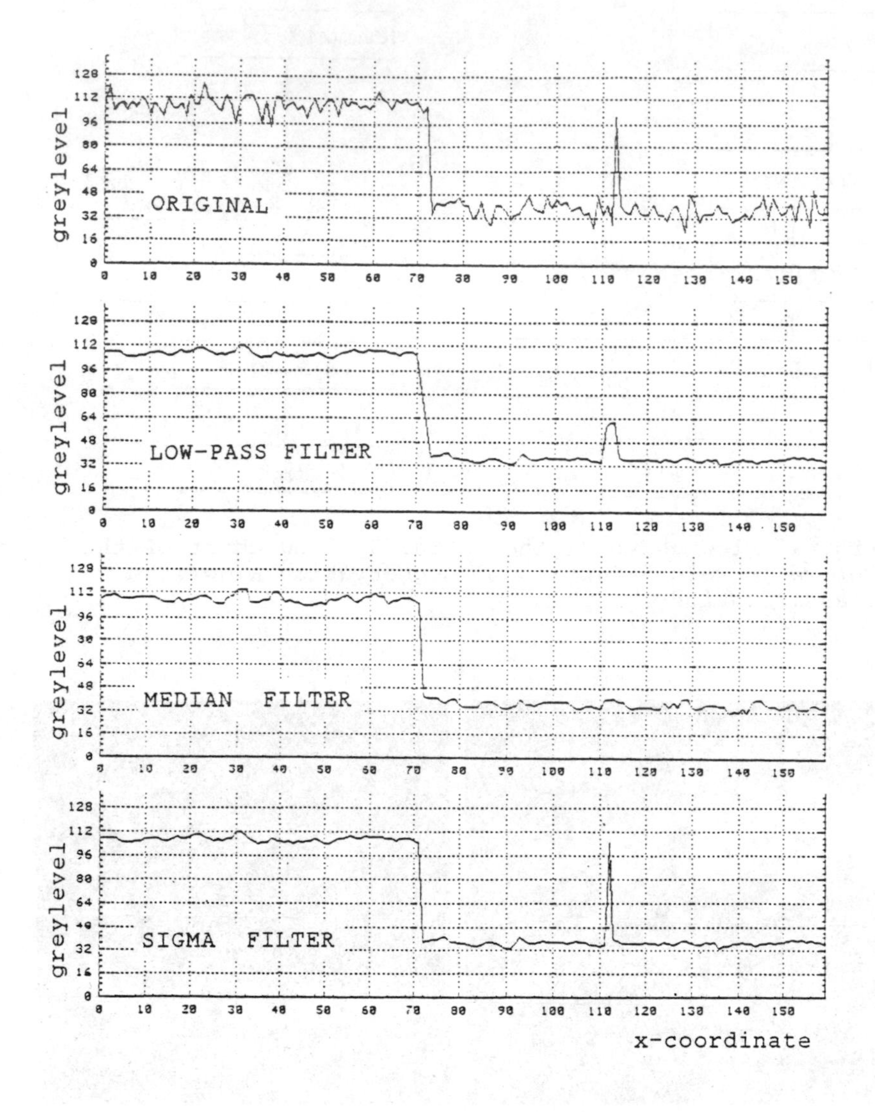

Fig. 2 Results of three filters

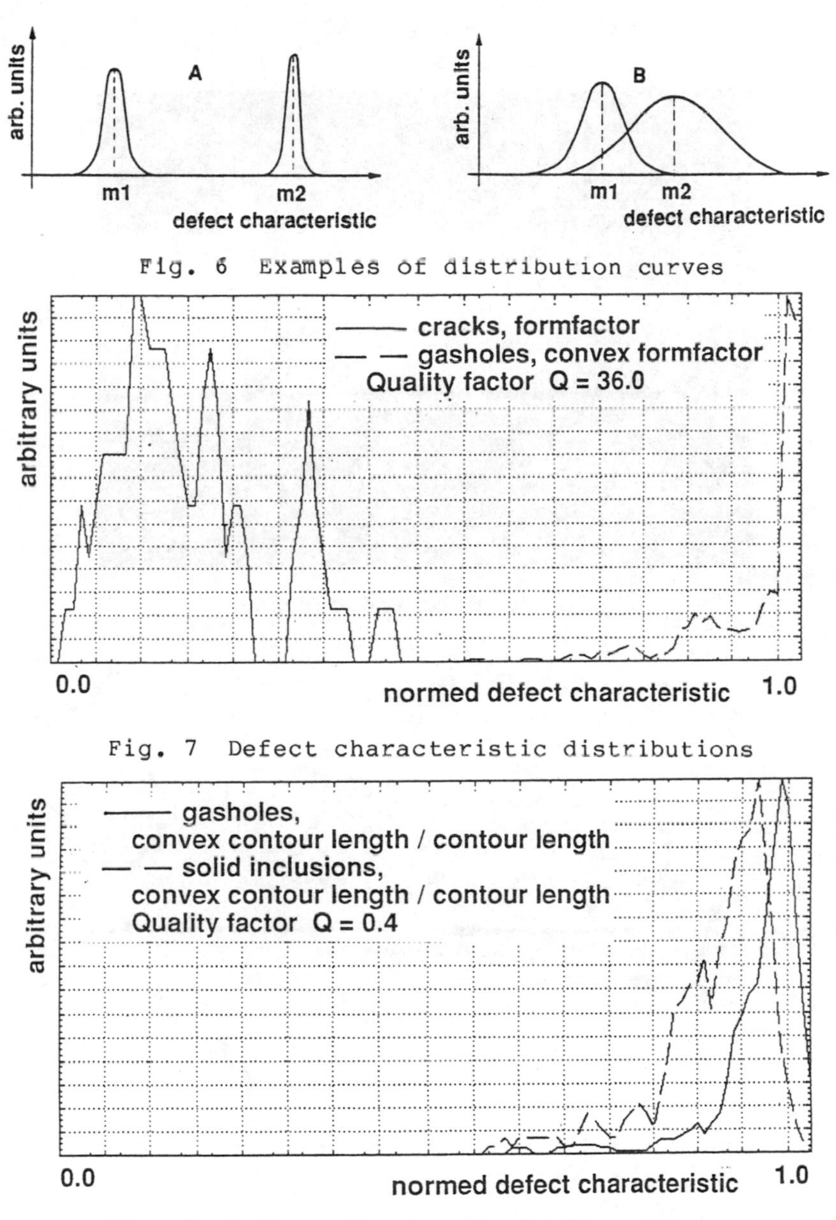

Fig. 6 Examples of distribution curves

Fig. 7 Defect characteristic distributions

Fig. 8' Defect characteristic distributions

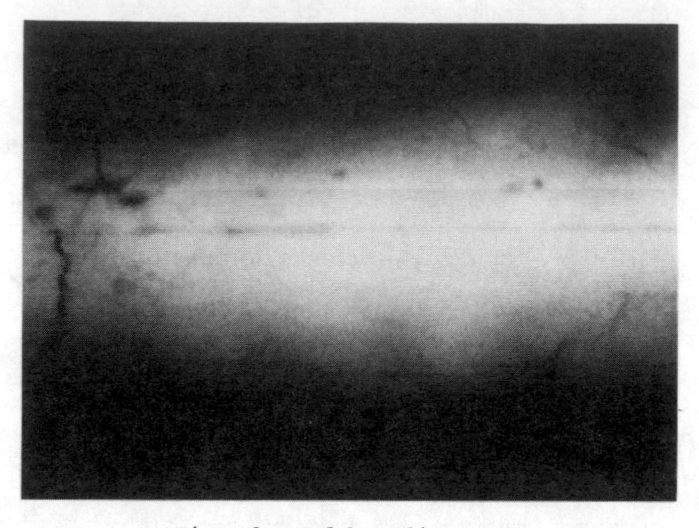

Fig. 9 Weld radiograph

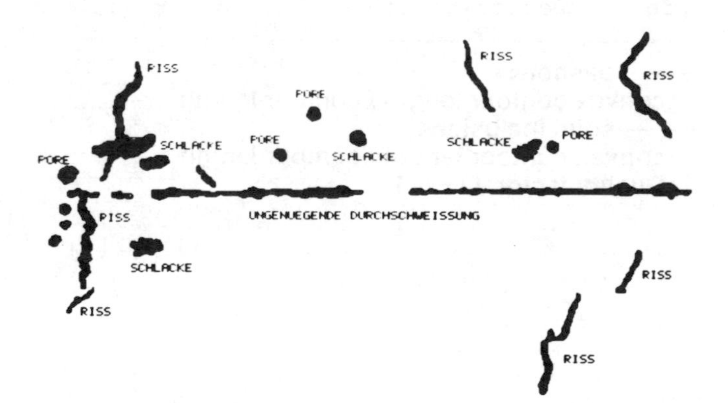

Fig. 10 Classification result

IMAGE PROCESSING-AIDED RADIOMETRY

G BASLER

This paper describes the possibilities of radiometric measurements resulting from an application of real-time radiography together with digital image processing.

By utilizing the possibilities the X-radiography allows, the calibration of parts lying within the materials can be made visible without any demounting work.
For these measuring and calibrating operations a specific radioscopic system was developed which will be described under special consideration of the applied methods for the calculation of the location of structures contained in video images by the aid of digital image processing.

X-Rays used as Measuring Means

The quality of X-rays to penetrate material and thereby being attenuated, give the possibility to use the rays for measuring hidden structures which are not accessible by light optical or mechanical means.

Theoretically, the very short wave-length of the X-rays, compared with the visible light, allows extremely precise measurements. Unfortunately, their usability is limited owing to the following facts:

- The transparency of materials reduces the contrasts of structures to be tested.

- There are no effective optical components for X-rays that could be paid for, so that the display of a structure will always be the result of a central projection.

Dr G Basler, RICH. SEIFERT & CO.

- The intensity of the X-radiation which can technically be realised, measured by the number of quanta per solid angle and time, is extremely low when compared with the case for visible light.

On the other hand, for the determination of geometries with X-rays, there are some degrees of operational freedom which cannot be realised by other methods of non-destructive testing.
Usually, a high spatial resolution of the image is required only in the measuring direction; the resolution vertically to the measuring direction, however, is not critical. Furthermore, the object area which has to be displayed is very small or can be made very small by selecting the right measuring method.

When the imaging system is a combination of X-ray image intensifier and television camera, the image quality and the measuring resolution can be increased by measures as stated below:-

- The dimensions of the focal spot of the X-ray tube can be reduced without any loss of intensity in the measuring direction by reducing the target angle of the X-ray tube - Fig.1.

- The reduced focal spot allow a corresponding geometric magnification, until the geometric unsharpness is approximately equal to the interior unsharpness of the input screen of the X-ray image intensifier tube - Fig.2.

- When using the same output diameter screen, a reduction of the effective input screen diameter by electronic methods reduces the influence of the interior unsharpness of the output screen.

- By selection of the focal lengths of the lenses, an optical magnification of the output image of the X-ray image intensifier allows the reduction of the influence of the interior unsharpness of the television pick-up tube.

- Furthermore, by selecting an image intensifier tube with a thinner scintillation screen, the spatial resolution of the entire system can be improved.

Measuring Problem

A concrete example will demonstrate the limits and possibilities of measuring a structure with X-radiation.

A tubular geometry (picture 3) consisting of two nearly concentric elliptic tubes and one so-called heating tube are to be tested. The distance between the heating tube and the interior tube has to be determined. With respect to the measuring problem, the relatively large wall thickness of the outer tube and the extremely small wall thickness of the interior tube and the heating tube are an unfavourable condition.
A further impediment is the fact that the interior tube is made of a low absorbing material which is displayed at only a very low contrast.
The effective wall thickness in radiation direction which is displayed in picture 4 does not consider this fact.

Owing to the thick-walled outer tube the spectrum of the X-radiation will be considerably hardened, so that the structures to be measured will be imaged with a very low contrast.
With a total diameter of the tube system of approximately 220 mm the determination of the distance to be found had to be made with a maximum tolerance of ± 50 µm.

Measuring Principle

It seems reasonable to display the interesting area, to determine a scale factor, and to take the required measurement from the image (picture 5).

This method, however, has the following disadvantages:

- The scale factor depends on the operating parameters and on the geometric errors of the imaging system and is, therefore, neither time constant nor isotropic.

- Owing to the geometry, the interior contour of the interior tube is unsharply displayed and the visual determination of its location is practically impossible.

- Since, with respect to the outer tube, the location of the interior tube is not exactly known, also the effective geometric magnification is unknown which is another uncertainty for the scale factor.

- The absolute accuracy depends on the size of the sample.

The disadvantages stated above can be avoided if the measuring is made by a parallel displacement of the central beam in relation to the object and the displacement itself is taken as the measure.
This way, all disadvantages are eliminated which might be caused by the central projection, geometric variations or by varying the imaging scale.

Principally, there are no limitations with respect to the imaging scale, because always only the contour to be measured has to be imaged.
Because the interior diameter of the interior tube and also the diameter of the heating tube are well known and the location of the interior contour of the interior tube is very hard to determined, we proceeded as follows:

The direct measuring of the distance between interior tube and heating tube is replaced by the determination of the axis position of the interior tube and the position of the heating tube axis. Since the diameter of the heating tube as well as the interior tube diameter are known, the required distance results from these measurements.
This measuring method does not make it necessary to take the poorly contrasting interior wall of the interior tube as a reference. It is sufficient to determine the centre of gravity coordinate of the wall image or a similar feature.

Inspite of this measuring method, the visual determination of the spatial position of the inspected structures is practically impossible, because the given geometries supply an unsharp image very low in contrast. The application of an efficient image processing system and of specific image improvement and evaluation routines allowed the development of an interactive measuring procedure.
Below, the single steps of this procedure will be described.

As a first step the measuring plane is determined. This requires that the object is rotated until the distance between heating tube and interior tube is minimized.
This adjustment has to be made visually.

From now on, only translatory motions are made, normal to the direction of radiation.

The left wall of the interior tube is moved into the image center as closely as possible. The exact determination of the spatial coordinate of the interior tube wall is interactively made, supported by an image processing system at the following sequence:

1. At first the image is time-integrated (picture 6). The integration factor can be selected.

2. In a defined window, the image is then spatially integrated by averaging the grey values of the columns. The result is a single density curve for the window area almost free from noise (picture 7).
   The time integration and spatial integration are necessary because the original image is extremely noisy owing to the large total wall thickness and the extreme magnification.

3. For elimination of the shading a quasi-differentiation is made by subtracting the density curve from that density curve which is displayed by several pixels. Resulting are a maximum and a minimum by which the wall location is determined.

From the above, the computer calculates an assumed wall center and marks this calculated position with a cursor.

The operator moves the radiation axis (which means the X-ray tube and image intensifier together) until this generated cursor is in line with a firm cursor on the image (hardware cursor). The alignment will be acknowledged and the computer stores the position of the central beam.

After the central beam has been moved by the amount of the diameter of the interior tube, the spatial coordinate for the opposite wall image will be determined according to the same procedure.
The location of the axis of the interior tube will be calculated by averaging the two coordinate values. Systematic errors by the determination of the wall location are symmetrical to the tube axis and are thereby cancelled out.

After the real location of the interior tube axis is known the position of the heating tube section has to be determined.
The central beam is moved as closely as possible to the image center by toggle operation. The determination of the center of the heating tube section is also interactively made with the aid of the image processor.
After an integration of the image within a window by time and by columns, the grey shade minimum is determined for both the wall images, and the center is marked with a gene-

rated cursor. The operator moves this cursor to align with the hardware cursor and acknowledges the center position. Since, on account of the sample geometry, the density curve of the heating tube opening is asymmetrical in relation to the center of the opening, the measured value is systematically wrong (picture 4).
The grey shade minima are displaced by half a wall thickness in a direction towards the center. Accordingly, also, the section center is displaced by half a wall thickness of the heating tube toward the system center.
From a consideration of this effect the required distance between heating tube and interior tube can be determined.

Test Setup (picture 8)

Among other components, the test setup consists of two linear guidances which can be adjusted by D.C. motors by increments of 0.001 mm. The carriages of the linear units support the 160 kV X-ray tube as well as the combination of X-ray image intensifier and television camera.

The standard X-ray tubehousing with a 0.4 mm focal spot is tilted by approximately 16° effecting a line focus with the effective dimensions of 50 x 400 µm. This line focus is located parallel to the axis of the interior tube.

The X-ray image intensifier is a 17 cm SIEMENS image intensifier of the latest generation with an effective input field reduced to a diameter of 120 mm.
The object plane is selected in such a way that the geometric magnification of approximately 1:4 is produced.
The output image of the X-ray image intensifier is transmitted to the input screen of a PLUMBICON pick-up tube by a tandem optics with a focal length ratio of 1:1.5.
Owing to the stated ratios, the full image width on the monitor is identical with an object width of 11.5 mm.
This means a resolution of 22.5 µm per pixel, provided the image will be scanned with 512 x 512 pixels.

The output signal of the PLUMBICON is led to an image processing system which contains, besides a 0.5 MByte image memory, an image processor and is managed by a Host computer DEC LSI 11/73. An interface links the image processing system with the control of the machine.

The operator views the processed image (picture 9) of which the cursor has to be aligned with the hardware cursor.
As an aid he can use a route pointer which in a superproportional way displays the difference between actual

and nominal position.

The measuring system is applied in the production line and has, therefore, been designed as a fully protected equipment.
Owing to the large size of the objects to be measured and to the corrections to be made due to the measurements, the operator is seated on top of the radiation protection cabinet (picture 10).

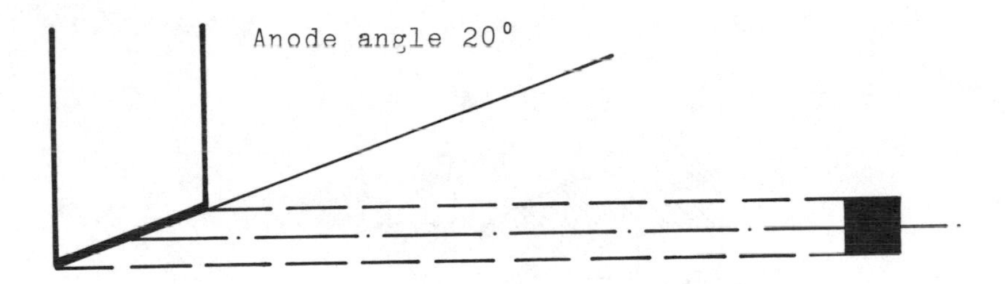

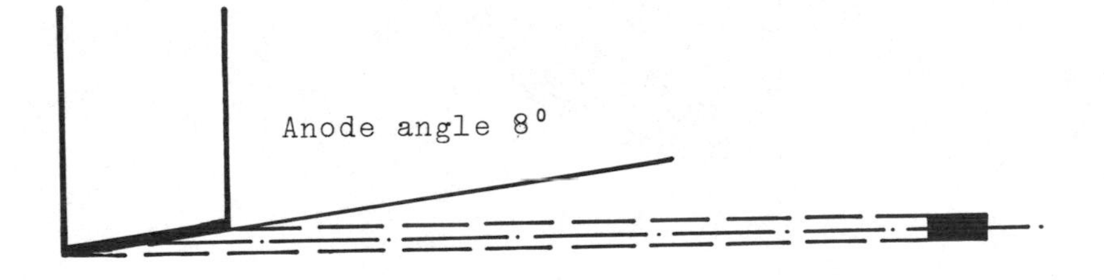

Fig.1

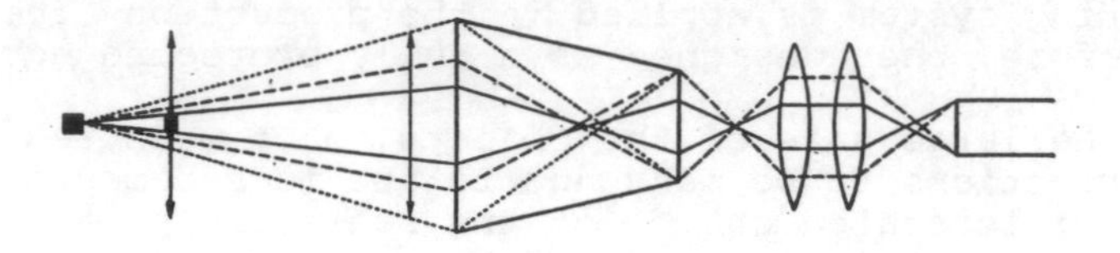

Fig.2. Optimising the resolution by magnification.

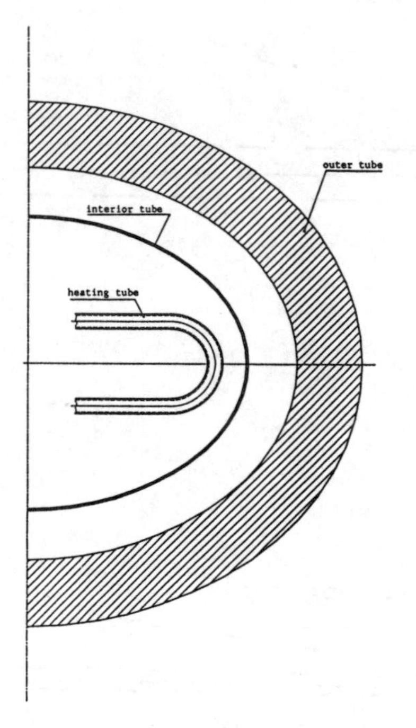

Fig.3 Object under test.

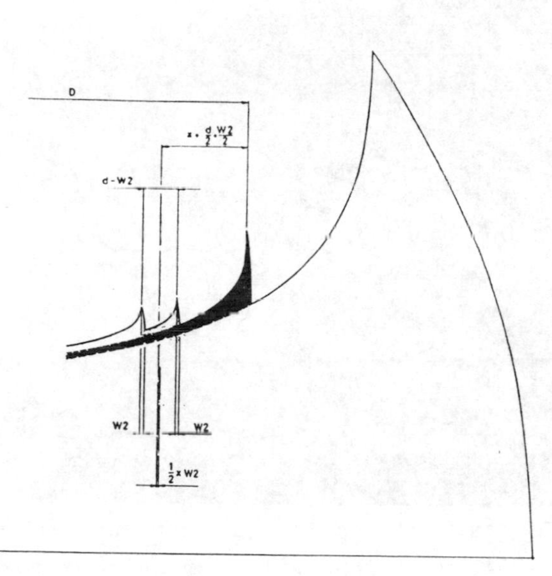

Fig.4. Effective wall thickness variations in the direction of the readiation beam.

Fig.5 Image of heating element and inner tube.
(Above): intensity variation across image.

Fig.6. Time-integrated image of inner tube.
(Below): intensity variation across image

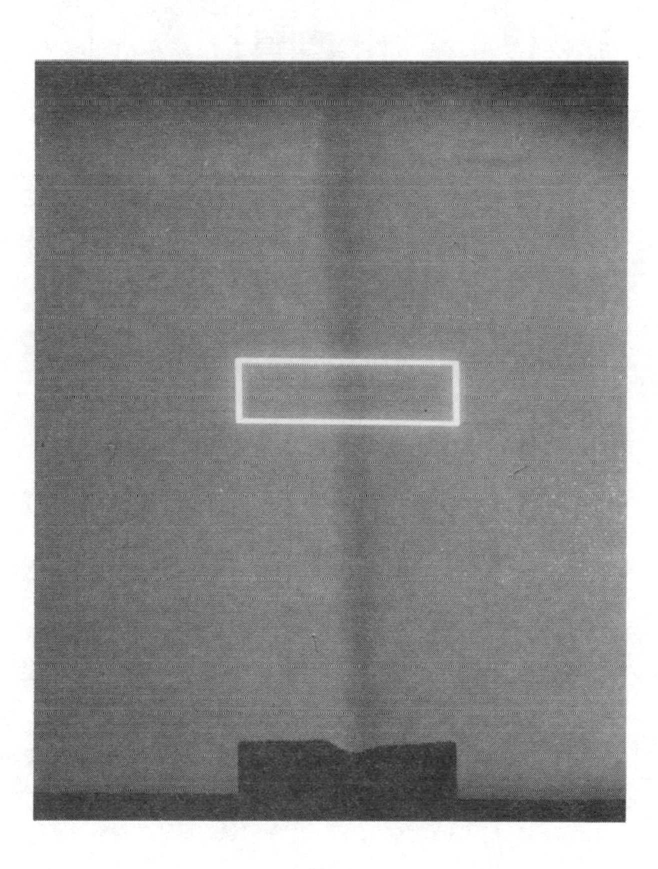

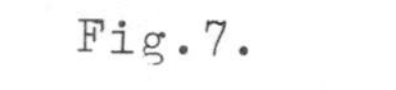

Fig.7.
Measuring window area on image of inner tube.

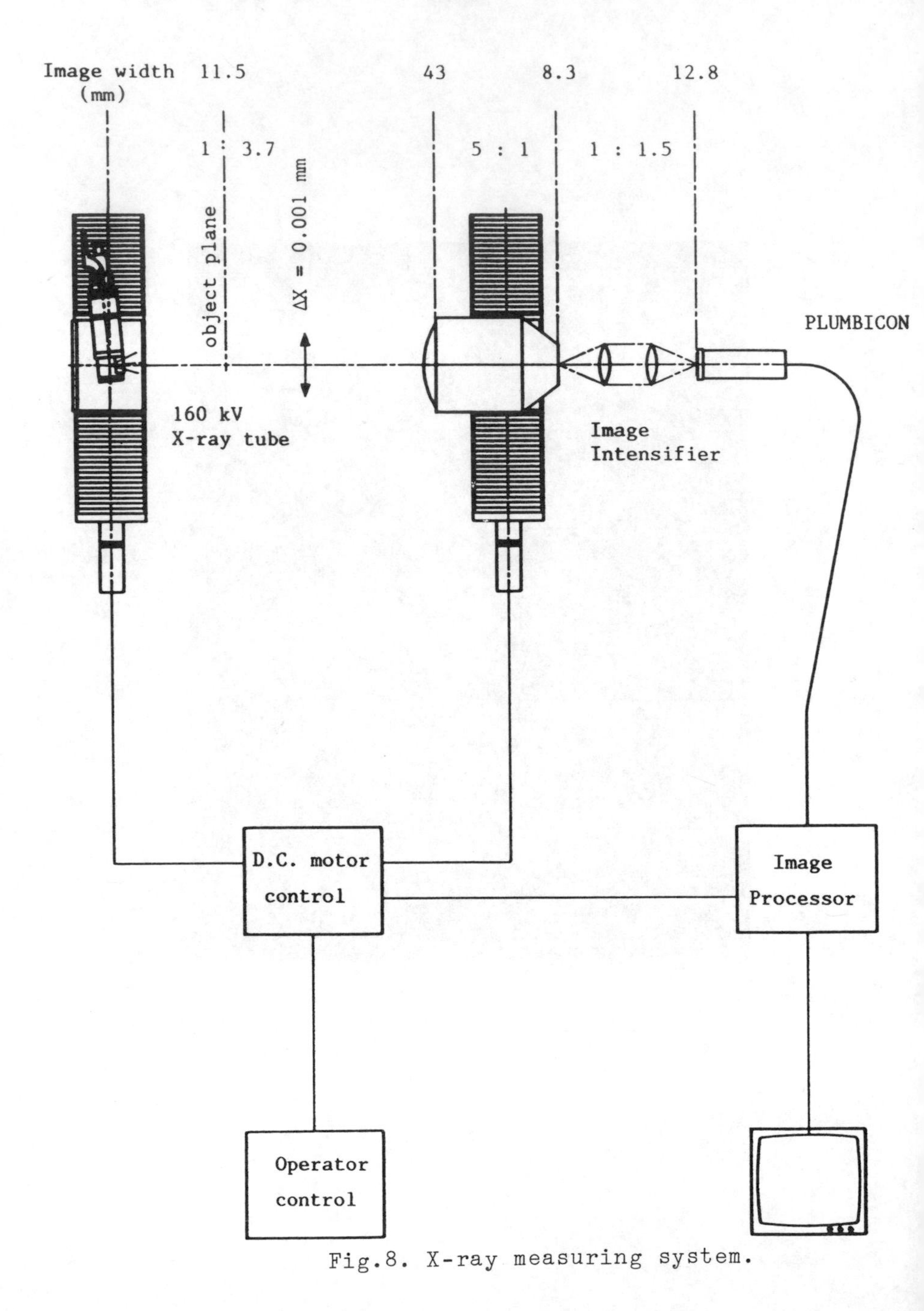

Fig.8. X-ray measuring system.

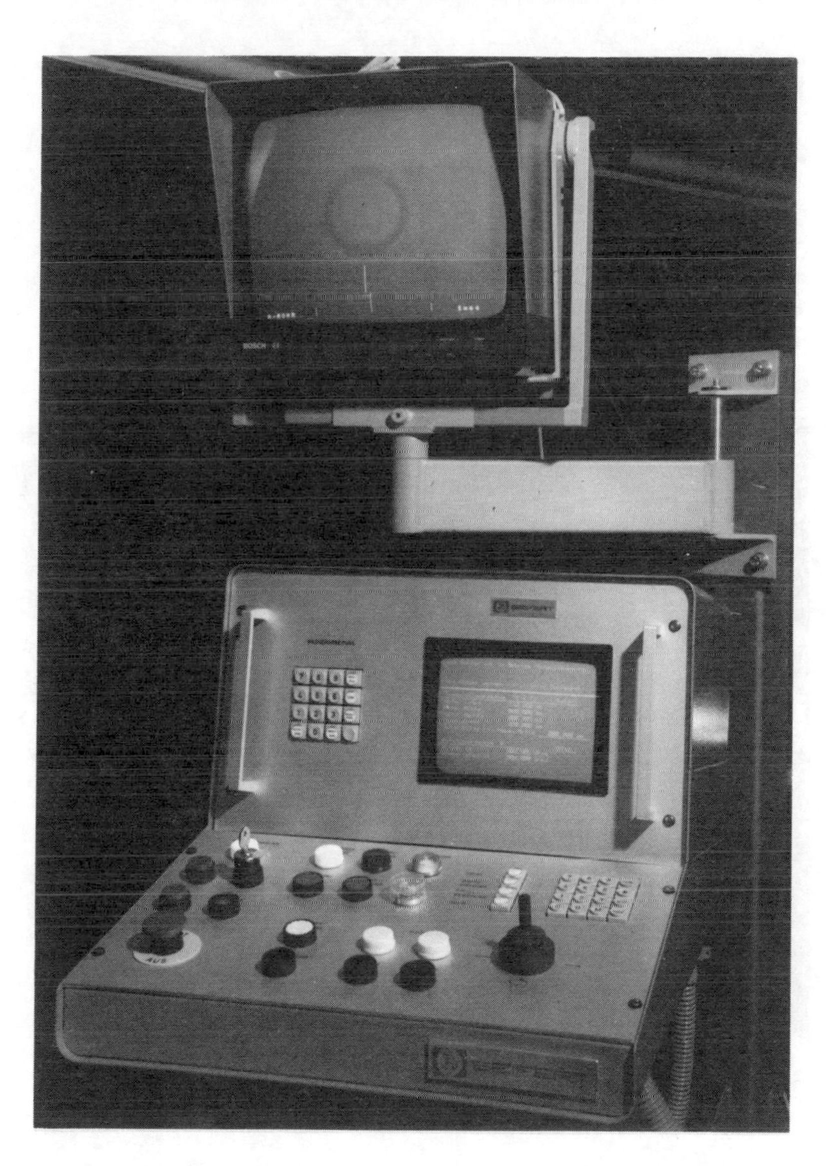

Fig.9. Control unit with monitor above showing displayed image.

Fig.10. Radiation protection cabinet, with control unit above.

IMPROVING IMAGES FROM REAL TIME RADIOSCOPIC SOURCES

David Throup

"Real Time Radioscopy" (RTR)using image intensifiers with x-ray sensitive primary screens have been in use for many years. So long in fact that some of the unwanted effects that they produce are taken as being a natural feature of real time radioscopic images, almost a fact of life. This paper introduces a method of improving the quality of RTR images through image processing beyond the traditional "noise reduction" not just for image intensifier systems but for any high sensitivity imaging system.

Introduction

This paper discusses some of the origins of sensitivity errors in image intensifier/camera systems as applied to "Real Time" radioscopy. These errors produce undesirable artefacts in the displayed image which limit the useful area of viewing and the diagnostic confidence in the result. The paper also proposes a solution based upon modern image processing technology and the cost benefits spinning out of applying the solution.

At the end of the paper there are several examples of before and after images to demonstrate the versatility of the proposed solution.

QUANTEL Ltd. Newbury England

The problem

The problem shows itself by distorting the grey level picture information of an image, resulting in a difficulty in interpretation and a restriction of the usable image area. This can be described as a sensitivity variation from point to point on the displayed image which in turn results in an uneven MTF (Modulation Transfer Function) with respect to position.

Taking the output of a camera/intensifier system used in an industrial radiography application as an example of a system which will introduce local area sensitivity and patterning errors, we can examine briefly the causes of these errors and thus propose a workable solution.

Fig 1. is a schematic of an image intensifier/camera system typically found in industrial/medical environments with the added sophistication of an optical splitter to feed film as well as a CCTV cameras.

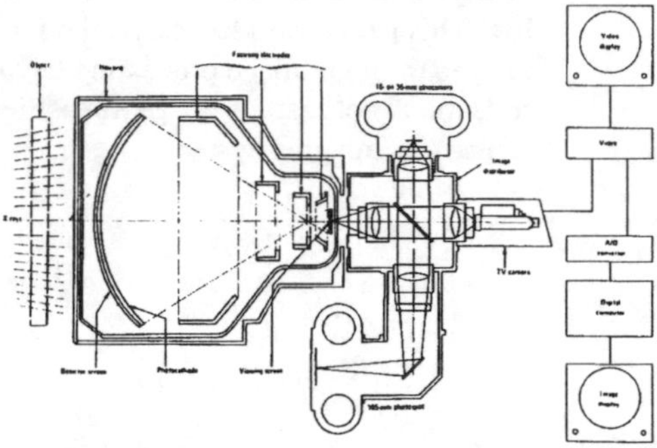

Fig 1. Schematic of an image intensifier system

The intensifier works by converting the X-ray photons transmitted by the specimen into electrons at the primary screen/photo cathode interface. These electrons are accelerated by means of a controlled electric field to a smaller fluorescent output screen. The brightness gain which can be several thousand is obtained partly from the size reduction and partly from the increased kinetic energy of the electrons.

Fig 2 shows diagrammatically the basic geometry of a real-time radiographic system. It shows the radiation source R, homogeneous specimen S and the primary image screen on the faceplate of the image intensifier I.

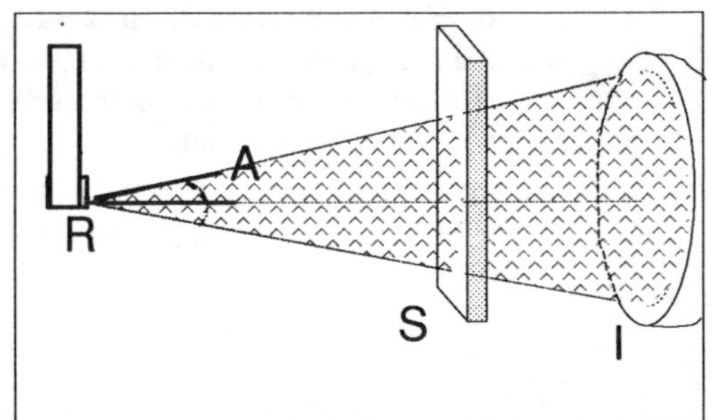

Fig 2. Simplified schematic of Radioscopic system

Assuming, for simplicity, that the intensifier and camera will generate an equal output from all points on its faceplate when presented with isotropic radiation normal to the primary screen, (an assumption that neglects the effects of wear and tear and manufacturing tolerance) . Fig 3 is an illustration of isotropic radiation in this sense.

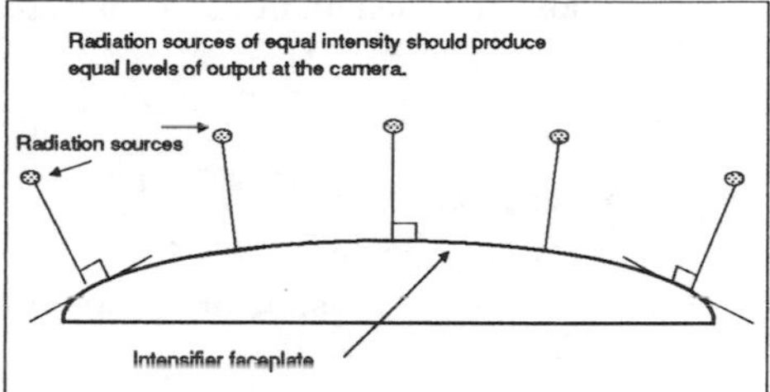

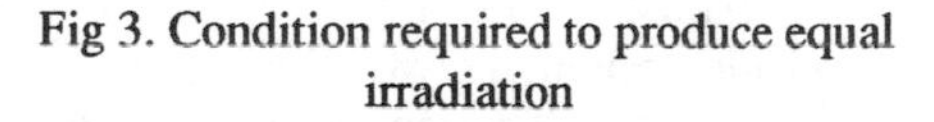
Fig 3. Condition required to produce equal irradiation

Finally, if the X-ray generator is assumed to be a point source then the following factors will control the system sensitivity .

1. The track length from radiation source varies from the centre of the primary screen to its edges.

$$\text{Intensity} \quad I=1/L^2$$

2. The track length through the specimen increases as the angle from the centre line increases.

$$\text{Apparent thickness} = \text{Thickness}/\text{Cos A}$$

3. The intensifier primary screen is not flat. This means that the circular radiation pattern at the centre turns into a longer ellipse the nearer to the edge of the intensifier we move. This results in a fall in output light intensity per unit area even though the radiation is passing through an apparrently thicker phosphor layer on the primary screen.

Fitting these factors into the imaginary but typical X-ray system shown in fig 2 enables the calculation of the likely errors due to each component and the net effect at any point on the screen. This will also show the relative significance of each of the errors.

1. The track length component.
The centre line length is defined as 1M. The angle projected by the beam striking the outer edge of the 15cm diameter intensifier is calculated as:

$$\tan A = 7.5/100$$
$$A = 4.25 \text{ Deg approx.}$$

Track length = (Centre length/Cos A) + allowance for curvature of the primary screen.

$$= 100/\text{Cos A} + 2.5 \text{ cm (estimated)}$$
$$= 102.775 \text{ cm}$$

Intensity of radiation related to 100% at the centre is:
I edge = $(100/102.775)^2$ = 94.67% approx

2. Extended track length through a flat specimen of thickness T.

Tedge= T/Cos a

= T * 1.0027

transmitted radiation = $e^{-1.0027}/e^{-1}$

= 99.73% approx.

3. Loss due to the curvature of the primary screen causing the finite point source to become spread into an elipse.
The angle subtended near the edge of the primary screen is measured at approximately 24 Deg from normal to the beam. The area covered by a circular radiation pattern increases by 1/Cos A approx. at small angles.

Thus area is increased by 1/(Cos 24)

= 1.094

= 92.2% of normal intensity.

In summary the sensitivity at the outer edge of the intensifier relative to the centre is reduced as follows:

Due to increased path length	94.67%
Due to increased thickness effect	99.73%
Due to screen curvature spreading the beam into an elipse.	92.2 %

Total = 94.67% * 99.73 * 92.2 = 86.9%

Calculating this for other points on the faceplate results in the traditional "dome" shaped sensitivity characteristic seen in all image-intensified images. A pseudo 3D plot of sensitivity of a new image intensifier is shown in fig 4. The X/Y axis represents the X/Y axis on the video monitor. The vertical Z axis is made to represent relative sensitivity.

This was produced by exposing the primary screen to radiation from a point source axially aligned with the centre of the intensifier. The height of the graph at each point XY represents the sensitivity at that point on the screen.

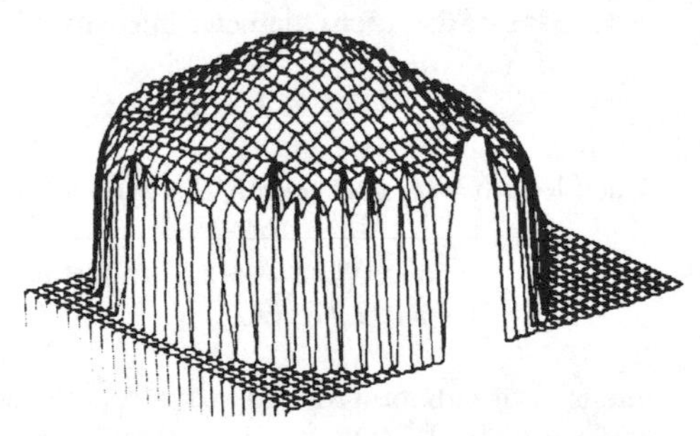

Fig 4. New intensifier sensitivity map

From this plot it is evident that some other effects are present as there is a distinct plateau area around the perimeter of the image. This may be due to some attempt at correcting the sensitivity in the camera part of this particular imaging system or, more probably, the effect of increased thickness in the conversion phosphor screen.

Consider now the output of an intensifier/camera system which has been in use for some months or years.

In fig 5., which represents the sensitivity map collected under the same general conditions as fig 4., it is evident that the simple geometric principles used to quantify the sensitivity of a new intensifier/camera system are no longer adequate. In this figure we can see irregular areas of low sensitivity and local "burn" marks which will cause severe grey level artefacts and variation of the MTF on any viewed image. The actual image output under these conditions is represented by fig 6.

To add to these problems it is desired to examine circumferential welds in a 24" steel pipe using the "Double Wall Single Image" DWSI technique. This is shown diagrammatically in fig 7.

An additional source of sensitivity loss is shown by this technique. It takes the form of an exaggerated loss due to the apparent increase in thickness of the pipe wall at the edges of the image due to the curvature of the pipe wall.

For small diameter pipes, where the pipe diameter approaches the diameter of the primary screen, this "thickening" can effectively more than double the apparent thickness of the pipe wall.

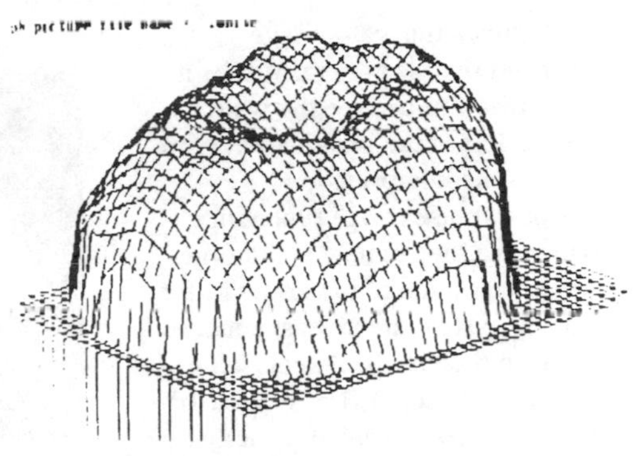

Fig 5. Sensitivity map of a used intensifier

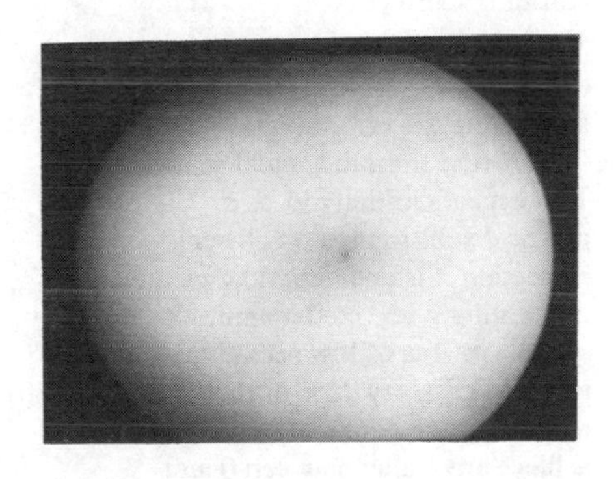

Fig 6. Image of 24" pipe wall through well used intensifier

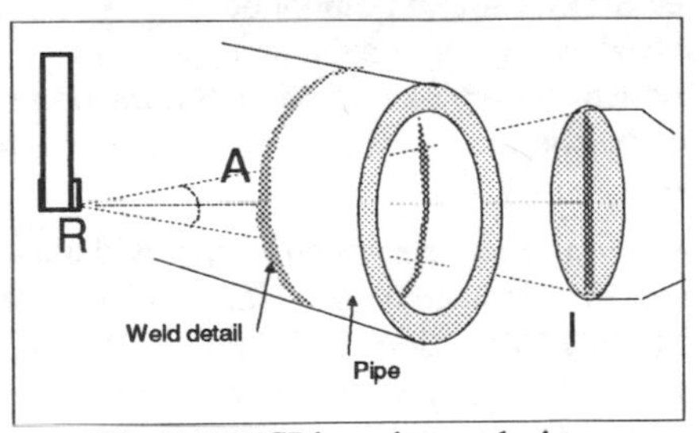

Fig 7. DWSI imaging technique

Fig 8. shows the weld image generated by this system. Whilst it is true that you can see the weld, much is left to the imagination with regard to its interpretation. Attempts to use image processing to improve the contrast are doomed as the magnitude of the errors in the imaging system are at least equal to the magnitude of the defects which need to be detected. The graphic of fig 9. shows the problem exactly.

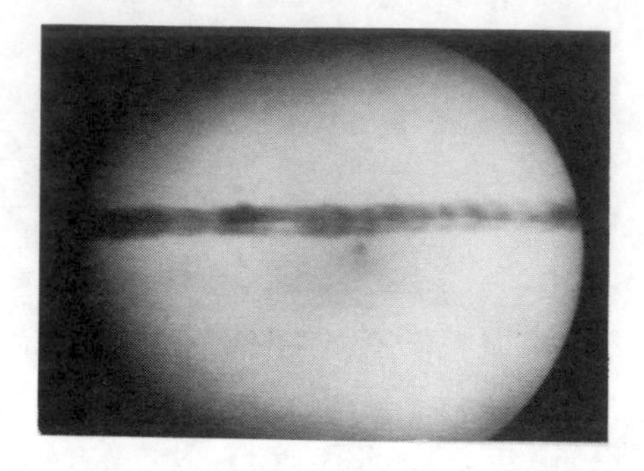

Fig 8. Weld image DWSI through well used intensifier

The Solution

The solution to the problem is a technique which we shall call "Shading Correction".

Some experiments have been carried out on the basis of subtracting the error image information from the actual image. This appears initially to be a practical solution but on closer inspection it is apparent that we are not dealing with fixed magnitude errors. An area of low sensitivity (lower MTF), say 75% of that at the most sensitive part, can only achieve any value between 0 and 75% of the output at the most sensitive part. Thus the problem of sensitivity variation cannot be solved by adding or subtracting a constant at each picture point. Subtraction is only valid as a technique for correcting for the non-excited (black level) errors from the system which can be treated as constant data.

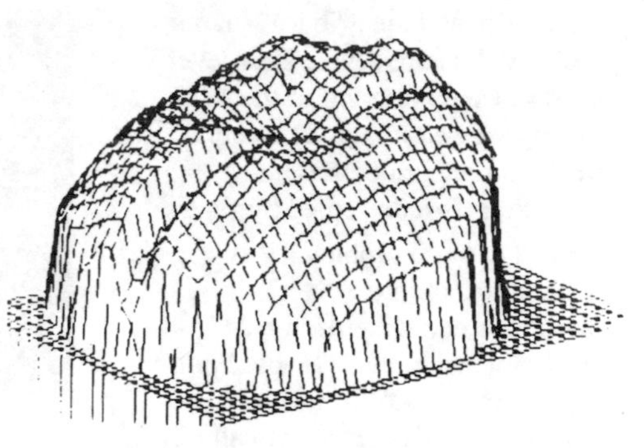

Fig 9. Sensitivity map of fig 8 shows irregular weld detail

What is needed is a system which will adjust and equalise the sensitivity of every point in the image field against a reference map of sensitivity. This is the process of "Shading Correction" built into the Quantel Sapphire scientific image processing system. This refined process consists of the subtraction of a "no radiation" reference from all further input, to re-establish a black level from which accurate sensitivity measurements can be made. This is followed by a pixel by pixel sensitivity correction value calculated from a reference image taken from a radioscopic image of a featureless piece of material nominally representing the radiographic density of the pieces to be tested.

By taking the active reference in this way the sensitivity of the system at a particular radiation energy level can be mapped. Experience with this technique shows that there is in fact a wide tolerence to radiation energy changes so it is not essential to stay fixed at one level for this process to give highly beneficial results.

Thus the displayed pixel value = (I - Offset) * G

I = Input value at pixel X,Y

Offset = Black level error at pixel X,Y

G = Sensitivity correction factor for pixel X,Y

This may seem a complex process to be applied to every point in the image, but it is in fact very straightforward to set up and use.

All that is required is to noise reduce the input image with the X-ray generator turned off and command the system to store it as a "Black Reference". Now turn on the X-ray generator and make an image through a featureless piece of material broadly representing the type of material to be examined. Noise reduce this and save as a "White Reference". The Sapphire system will do the rest - in real time.

A further and perhaps more significant benefit in some applications would be that the reference material need not be flat. If it copies the profile of the actual specimen then, as in the pipe weld case, it can compensate for errors caused by the specimen shape. Thus it will increase the sensitivity towards the perceived edge of the pipe.

Using this process it is possible to convert the "dome"of fig 5/6. into an ideal flat field of fig 10/11. and the uncorrected image of fig 8,9. into the gain and offset corrected image shown in fig 12,13.

These processes being carried out in real time present a significant improvement in radioscopic quality.

The benefits

Using this technique presents the user with several quantifiable benefits which can result in a positive payback on the investment involved. Listed below are some of these benefits but new ones are being generated constantly as the technique is applied in research environments.

1. The full area of the intensifier primary screen can be used for the evaluation of detail.

2. Image "mottling", burn marks and blemishes are removed leading to the ability to perceive finer image detail.

3. Sensitivity over complex and curved surfaces can be automatically corrected. Fig.14

4. Intensifier/camera life is considerably extended.

5. Densitometric measurements can be confidently taken at any point on the screen.

6. Automated analysis becomes more practical as features become more predictable over the field of view.

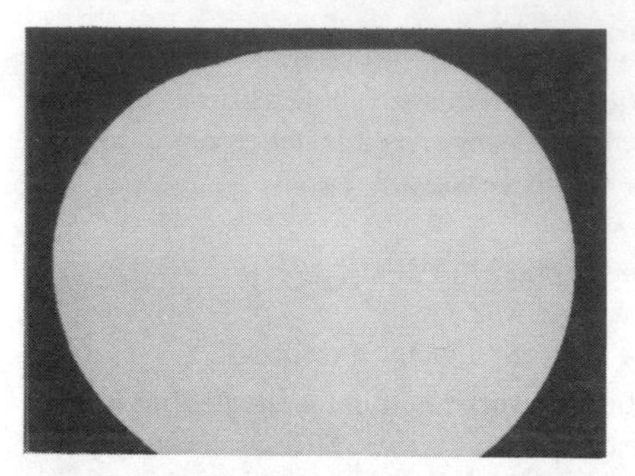

Fig 10. Shade correction applied to Fig 6.

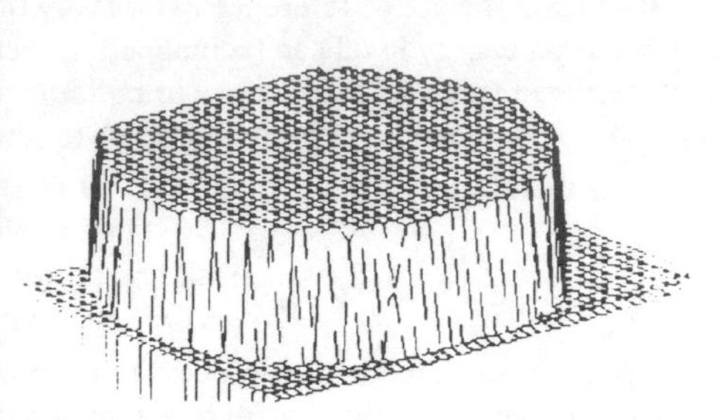

Fig 11. Shade correction applied to fig 5.

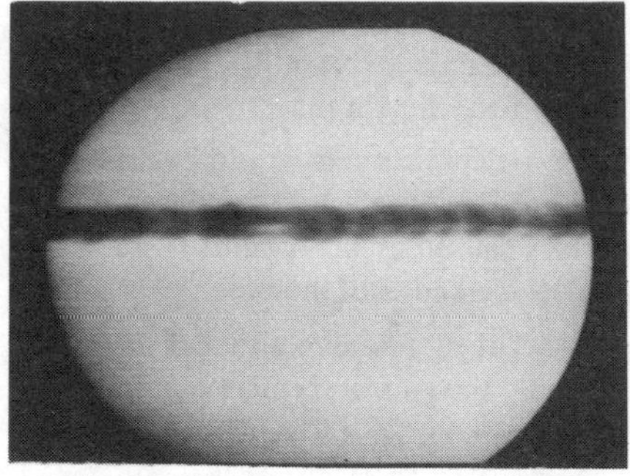

Fig 12. Shade correction applied to Fig 8

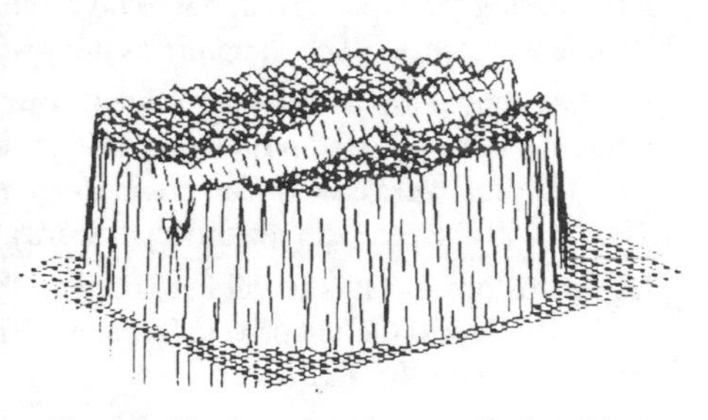

Fig 13. Shade correction applied to Fig 9.

Summary

The process of "Shading Correction" is a significant step in improving the viewed quality of video "real time" X-ray images. Used in conjunction with noise reduction and contrast stretching it extends the usable primary screen area of the intensifier to the whole screen from the centre portion which was the previous limit of use.

The extension of service life of the intensifier should provide a financial justification for looking seriously at this technique. It is quite possible that the cost of Sapphire can be recovered well within the service life of the system just by using this "Shade Correction" technique.

This moves "Image processing" into a positive payback situation where it actually contributes to company profits in a readily identifiable way augmenting the quantifiable product quality inspection benefits.

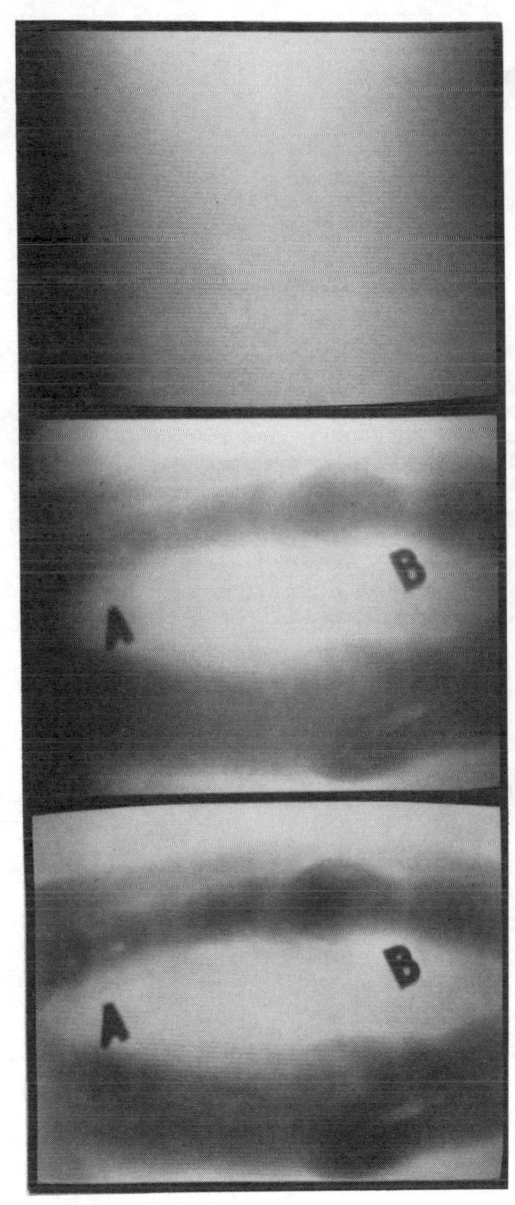

Fig.14

Off screen photograph showing a radioscopic noise reduced image of a section of stainless steel pipe 60mm diameter.

This shows clearly the darkening effect at the left and right edges caused by the apparent thickening of the pipe as seen by the image intensifier.

This is an example where we can see the combined effects of intensifier distortion and subject distortion.

The weld image has to appear through the sum of these distortions.

Using the first image as a system sensitivity map enables us to correct the weld image.

The result shown in the lower photograph enables much more of the weld to be examined from any individual angle.

This should result in faster inspection times and greater detail present in the image.

REAL TIME X-RAY SYSTEM WITH FULLY AUTOMATIC DEFECT DETECTION AND QUALITY CLASSIFICATION.

Kim Demandt and Lars Kai Hansen,

0. ABSTRACT

There is an increasing interest for fully automatic inspection systems.

Real time X-ray systems are in principle well suited for automation. Manipulation and system control can be automated using robotics. A real-time image can be digitized and analyzed by modern image processing algorithm for automatic defect detection in high-speed computers. However, X-ray images of real objects are often much more complex and difficult to analyze than most visual images in normal machine vision applications. New modern non-trivial algorithms such as neural network and simulated annealing will have to be applied.

In this paper the system design and the computational aspect of fully automatic X-ray inspection is presented. Results from a study of automatic X-ray inspection, using non-trivial image processing on complex Al-castings, will be given.

1. INTRODUCTION.

Real-time X-ray or fluoroscopy has become a well-established technique for Non-Destructive Examination (NDE), with major applications in:

* Weldings
* Castings
* Nuclear
* Aircraft
* Food
* Pharmaceuticals
* Electronic
* Defense

Andrex NDT Systems, Copenhagen.

There is a growing interest in automation of the examination process. This is motivated by several factors:

* Increase in examination speed.

* Quantitative and reliable examination.

* Elimination of costly routine work.

The need for fully automatic inspection will probably increase in the future, due to more and more 100% on-line control, as a consequence of fully automatic production, where no human beings are left for monitoring the process.

Real-time systems are in principle particularly well suited for automation. Real-time images can easily be digitized, and operating with digitized images we can invoke modern computers for image analysis and statistical inference.

The material handling equipment, manipulation and X-ray can be controlled using robotics, PLC's etc.

In this report we shall present the basic components entering a modern real-time system. Our main topic is, however, to discuss the problems faced in designing the image analysis algorithms and the decision systems necessary for solving the complex task of X-ray examination.

For the examination of many industrial products such as castings, ammunition, electronics and weldings we shall argue that new computer-intensive methods have to be invoked. These new approaches are based on studies of the human visual system and formulated in terms of "Neural Network" models.

2. QUALITY ASSESSMENT IN X-RAY IMAGING

2.1 The real-time X-ray image

An X-ray image is generated by central shadow projection of the X-ray focal spot and contains information on the radiation distribution in the volume between source and image surface. The X-ray image is converted into a digital image through a long chain, consisting of an X-ray image intensifier, optical lens system between camera and intensifier, video camera and analogue to digital converter electronics. The X-ray projection and the different elements in the chain will in some or another way give a distortion of the ideal image.

The exponential absorption of X-ray, nonuniform conversion in the image intensifier and vignetting in the optics will contribute to an uneven illumination. Focal spot size and limited spatial resolution in X-ray image intensifier and camera system will give unsharpness; sharp edges will be smooth, due to the X-ray beam angles and the quantum statistics for X-ray photons will cause noise in the image.

Compared with many optical images a real-time X-ray image has a rather poor quality:

* noisy
* unsharp
* smooth edges
* nonuniform illumination
* superimposed image

2.2 Quality assessment from an X-ray image

The quality of an object is determined from analyzing the defect pattern in the image. Hence the quality assessment consists of two steps

1. Detection of defects.
2. Evaluation of the detected defects and its influence on the quality.

As nearly all X-ray inspection and standards have been based on a human interpretation of what is a defect and how a certain defect influences the quality, it is not always obvious how to make a computer program capable of replacing the human judgement.

The normal meaning of "image" stands for something not very well-defined which needs to be interpreted in a "human" process, where plausible constraints and additional information (experience) is added. The amount of extra information needed will depend on the type of object to be examined, as illustrated in figure 1.

2.3 The false reject problem.

Due to economic reasons fully automatic X-ray inspection is most relevant for large scale operations, where a large number of objects will have to be inspected, such as Al-castings, weldings, electronics and food.

The question is often asked: "How many defective parts will be accepted in a fully automatic system". The logical answer to this question is: "No parts with defects will be accepted, we just set the machine to reject the whole batch".

The question should be: "If we allow that a certain percentage of parts with defects are accepted, what percentage of parts without defects will be rejected and what is the largest defect which may be accepted under the worst circumstances".

It is of very little interest to have an equipment for inspection of 100 parts an hour if 20% of the parts are incorrectly rejected. The false reject rate is to a large extent determined by the "intelligence" of the algorithm for the defect detection and quality assessment, as it is normally assumed that all other parameters are optimal. On the other hand, when parts such as castings for cars, ammunition or aircraft components are X-rayed, as is quite often necessary due to safety aspects, so the rate of non-rejected defective parts must be minimized as well!

The false reject rate and the non-reject rate can be estimated only by experiments, by running a certain number of non-defective and defective parts through an equipment and counting the number of rejected and accepted parts. See figure 2. The vertical distance between the two curves for respectively false reject and correctly rejected should be as large as possible. However, more important is a distinct steepness. Soft curves will always give a problem in minimizing both the number of false reject and the number of non-rejected defective parts.

2.4 Conclusions

All odds seem to be against a real-time X-ray system with fully automatic quality assessment - a difficult and complex image, less defined analysis criteria and requirements for both minimal false reject rate and maximal true reject.

However, realizing the true complexity of the problem is the first step in solving the problem.

As most of the relevant real-time applications will be dealing with complex images, which have to be analyzed in a "human" way, it has been chosen to use modern non-trivial image analysis algorithms such as Neural Network in the automatic quality assessment process.

3. THE HARDWARE ENVIRONMENTS

To obtain maximum flexibility, a very modular concept has been developed. A typical modern real-time X-ray system as outlined in figure 3. consists of the following basic subsystems:

a) **Robot Controller.**
The robot controller has three purposes:

1. To work as the central brain for the whole system and send commands to the subsystems and keep them synchronized.

2. To control the geometrical axis of the part manipulator.

3. Operator-machine communication.

A real-time examination of a complex critical part can be a rather intricate and time-consuming task. The part will possibly have to be examined in many different settings of each of the systems components. As the number of human errors drastically increases with the number of control parameters, the robot controller is needed to ensure maximum reproducibility and reliability. The robot controller may in several cases be used to replace complex mechanical axis interlock systems f.ex. to assure that the X-ray tube and the X-ray image intensifier are pointed at each other in a complex examination pattern with an electronically controlled axis interlock system. The robot controller has an interface for shifting the mode of operation between: "manual", "learning", "editing" and "automatic".

b) **X-ray Source.**
The quality of the X-ray source is, of course, of utmost importance for the quality of the raw image. As in all machine vision applications, optimising the image can simplify the automatic assessment task. For optimal X-ray quality high frequency generators are normally used. An important parameter is the focal-spot size. Open microfocus X-ray equipment may be needed to obtain a high definition image for optimal crack sensitivity in ceramics or weldings.

c) **Object Manipulator.**
The full virtue of real-time examination is captured by invoking a multi-axis high precision manipulator. Due to the exponential nature of X-ray absorption, positioning is critical. A slightly different angle between the X-ray beam and an edge can change the sharpness of edge in the image drastically.

d) **Image Sampling System.**
In most applications a standard X-ray image intensifier system is used. The X-ray intensity in the image plane is converted into a standard video signal by an X-ray sensitive image intensifier tube, an optical coupling device and a standard video camera. The parameters of the system (iris, magnification etc.) are under robot control. For the protection from hard radiation bypassing an irregular object, a motorized masking system under robot control is installed right in front of the imaging system.

For application in examination of electronics high definition X-ray sensitive vidicon cameras may be used.

e) **Video Image Processor.**
The raw real-time image-output of the image sampling system is not optimal for human nor computer inference, due to noise and various degradations (eg. the point spread function). Noise can in part be removed by averaging over a number of raw video frames, and furthermore the image information can be enhanced by various transformations. For manual inference the Video Image Processor has a number of preprogrammed linear transformations including look-up tables and convolutions. A look-up table is a single-pixel function by which the grey scale can be stretched and compressed in order to match the image information to the human visual system. Convolutions are linear neighborhood operations eg. spatial smoothing or edge-enhancement (numerical differentiation).

f) **Quality assessment processor.**
The most suitable processor for implementing "Neural Network" algorithms is under investigation right now. Several parallel computers and dedicated neural computers have been investigated. In the near future benchmark tests will be performed.

For the time being, the image handling ie. storing and further analysis, the digitized signal is read into the RAM memory of a microcomputer (MC68030) and further it can be transferred to a normal or optical disc system for long-time mass storage. For low cost mass storage the microcomputer can be used to control a video tape recorder using a database system for storing and retrieving of images.

There are basically two modes of operation with an automatic system as described above: Teach-in phase and Execution phase.

In the Teach-in phase the operator interactively settles the optimal parameters for a given application and the necessary statistics for the decision system are gathered (calibration, etc.). This information is sent to the robot controller, where it is stored.

In the Execution phase the system reproduces the examination scheme as laid out in the Teach-in phase by retransmitting the parameters to the individual subsystems, and for simple tasks it can decide on the quality and tag the sample with a quantitative measure of quality. For documentation all or a subset of the images examined can be stored as mentioned above on discs or video tapes.

4. THE IMAGE MODEL

Defects are contrast deviations from "the expected". Given "the expected" as an image of a defect free sample, deviations can be traced back to:

* Positioning tolerances

* Tolerances within the object itself.

* X-ray parameter fluctuations (mA,kV).

* Sampling noise (after averaging).

* Defects.

From a quality control point-of-view the defects form the signal that we want to detect, hence the first four points above can be considered as noise. Given a specific type of object and a given projection, then the image-to-image variation will be dominated by the two first.

We can propose a general, albeit qualitative, image model:

> The image can be separated into a large-scale structure, the background, which varies from sample to sample but preserves its main topology; and defects ie. local (pos./neg.) deviations from the background. The structure is infested with counting noise and fluctuations due to the allowed tolerances.

The image model holds for both castings and weldings. In the first case, strong density variations give a rich structure to the background with weak perturbations from sample to sample. In weldings the background has less contrast but higher irreproducibility in topology.

5. IMAGE ANALYSIS STRATEGY

The analysis of an X-ray image of an object can be separated into three steps:

1. Modelling the large scale structure (background).

2. Detection of local deviation from large scale structure.

3. Evaluation of the detected deviations; influence on the quality.

The target of the two first steps is a binary image which is "high" on the local deviations and "low" on the background large scale structure. This involves two-dimensional signal detection. Before invoking this step we have to eliminate the background intensity variation with a background model.

For both background modelling and signal detection there exist several alternative algorithms. Due to the very limited time available for the analysis tasks, one has either to choose very simple algorithms or to choose algorithms that can be implemented on parallel/dedicated computers. The former solution means limited reliability and hence cannot be used in general, the latter implies algorithms that can run massively parallel, as serial high speed computers are too costly.

As a general concept for producing massively parallel algorithms we use cost optimization. Many tasks within image analysis, decision making and control can be formulated in terms of cost optimization. In the last 5 years there has been an ever increasing interest in these methods following the advent of the "Simulated Annealing" concept. In particular this has brought in the powerful tools of statistical physics for application in information processing.

6. BACKGROUND MODEL.

The purpose of the background model is to eliminate the object from the image, leaving the defects as "islands" in a noisy "ocean". The basic strategy for the development of the model follows from a closer look at the main topology in the image to be examined.

As an example, the background in a casting consists of extended, smoothly curved surfaces separated by strong coherent variations ie. the edges. The location of the edges cannot be predicted due to positioning variations and tolerances, hence the first step is to locate these for a given sample. Following the location of the edges the algorithm estimates the surfaces connecting the edge regions using the cost function approach. As a final step the difference image is formed; in here the edge regions are put to zero thus giving no contribution to the signal detection routine.

It is evident from the presentation of the image formation above that there are several uncontrollable factors entering the process. Of these factors some are truly stochastic, hence could be described by a noise model; but as we have argued, the most important factors are "systematic" perturbations originating in the positioning and parameter instability. It is, on the other hand, an experimental fact that the human visual system is "invariant" to these transformations, (ie. the classification is approximately independent of such perturbations).

Is it possible to formulate models with these properties?

In a situation without any specific model of the noise (nor the signal for that sake) we have obviously to rely on qualitative models. Such a framework is provided by cost optimization.

For background modelling we use cost optimization for estimating the smooth surfaces between edges. The dilemma we are facing is the following:

> We want to identify a smooth surface which is close (on the average) to the given noisy (rough) data.

If we denote the data by P(R), with R numerating the pixels, and the smooth target surface pixel by S(R) then the appropriate cost function has two terms:

$$\mathrm{COST} = \sum_{\bar{R}\bar{R}'} C(\bar{R},\bar{R}') \cdot \left[S(\bar{R}) - S(\bar{R}')\right]^2 + A \sum_{\bar{R}} \left[S(\bar{R}) - P(\bar{R})\right]^2$$

Both images are assumed to be quasi-continuous (real or high resolution integers) for the background model.

C(R,R') defines a neighborhood system for the smoothing term. Minimizing this term by itself, results in a uniform image. The simplest choice of C is the "nearest neighbors":

$$C(\bar{R},\bar{R}') = \begin{cases} 1 \text{ if } R' = R \pm(1,0) \text{ or } \bar{R}' = \bar{R} \pm(0,1) \\ 0 \text{ otherwise} \end{cases}$$

The A parameter determines the relative weights given to smoothing and the deviation term. For very large A, the deviation term dominates and the minimal cost is obtained for the trivial S(R)=P(R) solution.

By adjusting the two parameters C(R,R') and A, different types of background structures can be modelled in an optimal way. If the background structure consists of very steep edges, it has been found useful to clamp the model to those edges. Defects on edges will anyway be impossible to detect also for a human operator.

The background modelling is illustrated on figure 4, where a 1-D image (intensity profile) is used.

7. TWO-DIMENSIONAL SIGNAL DETECTION

We present in this section a new approach to the general problem of signal (defect) detection. The problem can be stated as follows:

> Given input data in the form of a signal (defect) infested with random noise and a back-ground model; produce binary output data being "high" on the signal and "low" on the back-ground.

Several classical methods such as single or dual thresholding can be applied. However, in several X-ray inspection problems we need more powerful (intrinsic non-linear) methods, to minimize the false reject rate, as thresholding often will be either too sensitive, too noisy, or not sensitive enough. See figure 5 and 7. The optimal solution is an algorithm, which takes all the signal information into consideration and not only signals below or above a threshold.

In the generic defect detection task we have only qualitative information on the geometry of the signal (it being higher/lower than the back-ground) so qualitative measures must be invoked.
- again we call upon the cost optimization method with a cost function of the general type:

$$\mathrm{COST} = \sum_{\bar{R}\bar{R}'} C(\bar{R},\bar{R}').\left[S(\bar{R}) - S(\bar{R}')\right]^2 + A\sum_{\bar{R}}\left[S(\bar{R}) - P(\bar{R})\right]^2$$

The major difference is that here we seek binary output (S =+/-1) as we are trying to identify the optimal binary approximation to the input.

With a binary output signal the complexity of the computational effort for obtaining S(R) increases greatly. From a simple quadratic optimization problem we enter the realm of combinatorial optimization.

This cost function is of the same form as the energy function for the "Random Field Icing Model" (RFIM) of amorphous magnetism. The physics of this model is briefly:

The local (atomic) magnets have magnetic moments S (quantum vector variables). The crystal fields "quenches" this vector into a single direction (uniaxial magnet) with two possible quantum states (spin 1/2 atoms). The electron exchange interactions favours alignment of neighbor magnets (cf. the first term of the cost function). Magnetic impurities produce static magnetic fields that locally influence the atomic magnets (second term) to favour a specific of the two fundamental states.

The local magnetic impurities can be compared with defects in an X-ray image.

The RFIM has been under intense investigation in recent years. One of the main problems has been to characterize the ground state ie. the state of lowest energy which dominates the low temperature behaviour. Simulated annealing has proven to be an efficient tool for solving this cost optimization problem. See figure 7.

8. THE QUALITY ASSESSMENT

The evaluation of the quality is made from two types of information:

1. Does the background model fit into the expected deviations from the ideal object ie. "Does the object look normal"?

2. Classification of the quality from the defect pattern detected.

In both cases the results (background model and defect pattern) will have to be compared with some sort of "model" for the object. In information processing it is important to note the distinction between soft and hard modelling.

The hard model

Given an accurate description of an information source, such a description can and should, of course, be used to formulate a mathematical model. With a model we can compress data and eliminate noise; in other words, operate with high reliability and minimum effort. Such a model has importance on its own, representing the system on a higher level of abstraction: "we understand the system and the processes that go on in it". This situation is familiar in fundamental sciences eg. in physics where the laws of physics are of a higher value than mere phenomenology. An important property of these "hard models" are their capability of extrapolation, you can predict the behaviour of a device that has not even been constructed yet.

The soft model

In a large number of science applications, however, we are faced with ill-defined systems. That is, situations where models are absent: "the system is too complex" or "we do not have the time for a complete description". Denoting the prior situation by "Hard Modelling" the latter calls for "Soft Modelling". Here we shall adhere to a pragmatic attitude trying to get around with statistical methods and fully empirical reasoning.

As pointed out in section 2 most real-time X-ray applications call for a "soft-model" due to the weakly defined accept/reject criteria. A soft model can be implemented in two ways:

1. The soft-hard way

The way an image is interpreted is forced into an mathematical algorithm using parameters such as number of defects, distances between defects of different sizes etc, combined with decision logic tree for saying good or bad.

There are certain obvious draw-backs of such a method:

a. Decision logic routines for analyzing the image will often be very complex and dedicated to only the actual application.

b. The quality assessment learning is converted into a computerprogrammers job.

c. If something falls outside the immediate expected,the soft-hard model has no common sense.

e. It is often tedious to make and test even small changes.

2. The soft-soft way

Supplementing traditional statistical methods there is a strong recent interest in the computational capacity of Neural Networks for discrimination and association. Being non-linear, the information processing of Neural Nets has some interesting features resembling primitive brain functions, and equally important, Neural Nets map naturally onto most parallel processing devices. See figure 8.

A typical soft-soft modelling case takes the following steps:

Decide the network	(degrees of freedom in the problem)
Teach-in	(Gather the training set)
Modelling	(Look for internal representations)
Consistency Check	(Intra- Training set vali-dation)
Prediction	(Model execution)
Long Time Consistency Check	(Is training set representative?).

The network structure has to be decided from the degrees of freedom needed. Most pattern recognition problems can be solved with relatively simple networks with one or two layers of hidden units.

The Teach-in phase covers calibration and optimization of parameters as judged by the examiner and, of course, collecting the training set. The training set consists of a number of samples complete with imagery and classifications.

During the modelling phase the system searches for representations of the hidden rules that entered the classification. The differences between various soft modelling approaches lie in their representation schemes. By definition, they have in common, though, that the optimal representations within a given scheme do not in any simple way relate to the underlying physical processes.

Sophisticated soft modelling methods have a number of consistency checks built in. The basic check (which actually in many cases is combined with the modelling phase) is an intra-training set consistency check. We here use the model on the training set itself (in statistics this is denoted "cross validation").

Yet another check can be performed during run-time. In course of prediction we test the input variation versus the variation found in the training set. It is important for the reliability of our soft model that the training set is updated if the parameters are drifting beyond the expected limits or if other "systematic" perturbations interfere.

9. THE COMPLEXITY OF CASTINGS EXAMINATION.

In this section we discuss the complexity of the validation and decision tasks that enter the examination of castings.

In particular we present a system for determination of "Regions of Interest" (ROI's) and for validation of edges and classification of defect distributions. Following the arguments of the preceding section we focus on algorithms that can be executed in massively parallel hardware environments.

By analyzing typical images of castings (see figure 9) the following examination scheme is proposed:

1. Domain segmentation

An X-ray image of a casting is normally dominated by isolated areas with a more or less uniform illumination surrounded by sharper edges. Those areas are called "domains". Due to tolerances mainly in the positioning of the object, the background model is clamped to the edges.

The domains are normally isolated using a simple gradient detection with a threshold, as we are only interested in the distinct edges. In some cases postprocessing like dilation/erosion might be needed to make consistent areas.

On figure A1 is shown a typical real-time image of an aluminum casting and on figure A2 its associated domain boundaries. The dark areas are the domains.

2. Windowing.

Positioning of region of interests (windows) relative to the domain boundaries.

By calculating the position of the domain boundaries one or several windows associated with each domain can be placed. At the moment rectangular windows are used. By associating the windows with the domain boundaries, the windows will not be sensitive to small deviations in the positioning of the object and will regulate their shape to the size of the domains.

Figure A2 shows windows laid in.

3. Difference image.

The domains between the edges are modelled using cost optimization. The major parameters are the weight between neighbor pixels (how much does it cost to have a different value of two neighbor pixels) and the weightfactor for not fitting to the pixelvalue in the image. This background modelling can in many ways be compared with fitting a "rubbersheet" with a certain stiffness to the overall topology of the domain in question.

The background model is subtracted from the original image and resulting in a difference image. The difference-image is shown on figure A3.

4. Binarization

   Generating a binary image giving conglomerated white areas (clusters), where the image is lighter (or darker) in certain area, than the average background.

   Simulated annealing is used to convert the difference-image into a black and white binary image. The simulated annealing can be compared with a partly "melting" down of the difference-image.

   Imagine that the difference-image is made of soft wax with a high surface tension. If the wax is warmed up just below the melting point all small deviations will smoothen out; however, the larger deviations will only be slightly deformed, due to the fact, that the surface tension will have less influence on larger conglomerated areas. See figure A4.

   A simple threshold conversion has shown to be very sensitive to noise. Considerable improvement can be obtained using dual threshold techniques. The dual threshold technique is several times faster than simulated annealing and can successfully be used in many less critical applications.

5. Cluster identification.

   Identification of the individual clusters in a window and associate some important data such as positions, areas, perimeters etc. to each cluster.

   The individual defects are found by using a mathematical algorithm "blop" to identify isolated islands. When the individual defects have been isolated, characteristic data such as position, area, perimeter etc. can be calculated.

6. Defect pattern recognition.

   Compare the "cluster pattern" data with a family of acceptable clusters made from a selection of good samples for accept or reject of the actual sample.

   Initial simple experiments with Neuron Network models have shown promising results. However, a further investigation will have to made.

The effect of the different steps is illustrated on figures A5 and A6, where intensity profiles are shown as well.

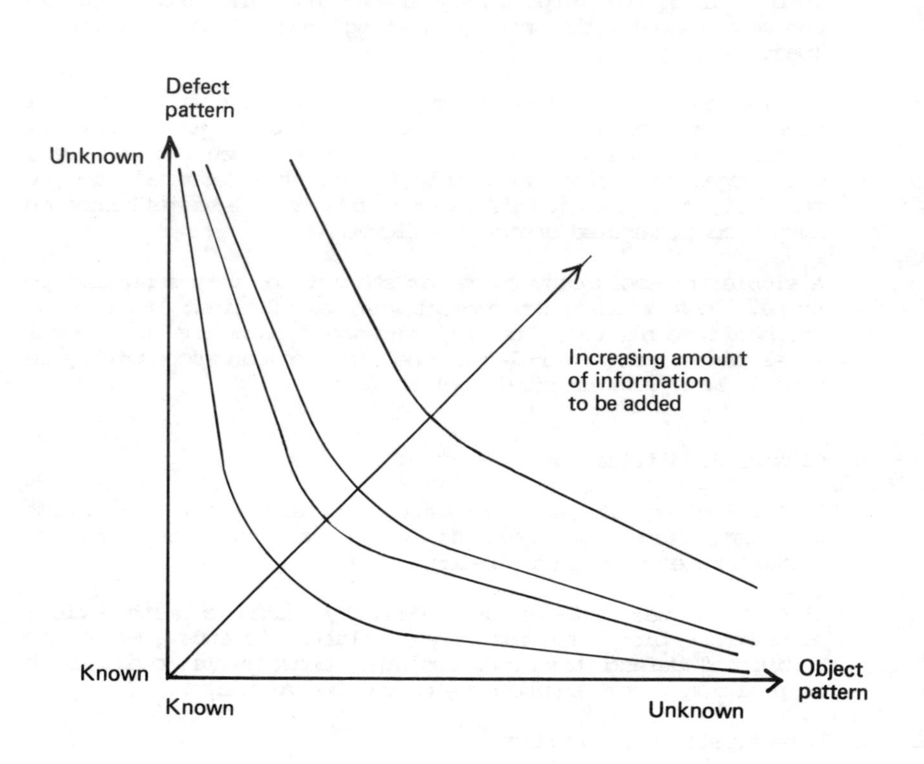

Fig.1. To interpret an X-ray image, plausible constraints and additional information will often have to be added.

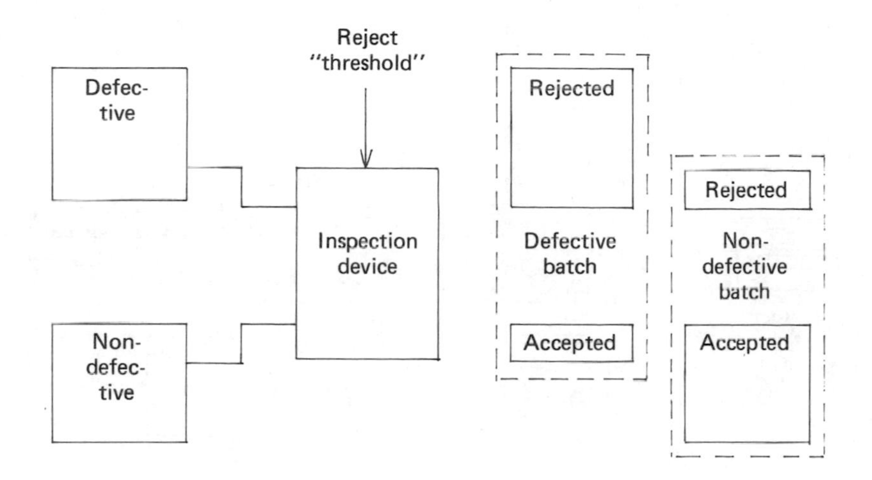

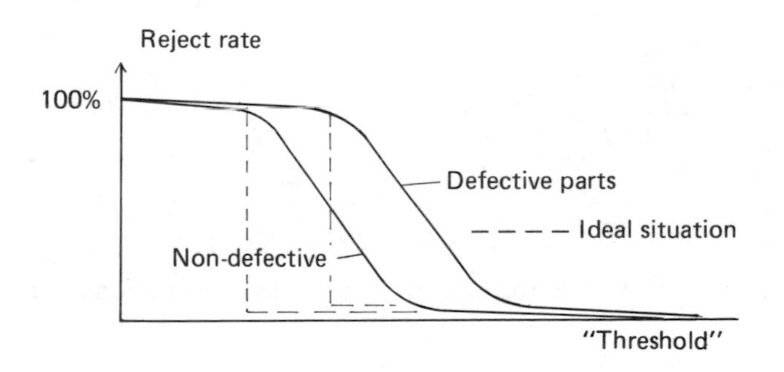

Fig.2. The false reject problem.
Without proper algorithms it might be impossible to obtain both a low false reject rate and a maximum rejection rate of defective parts.

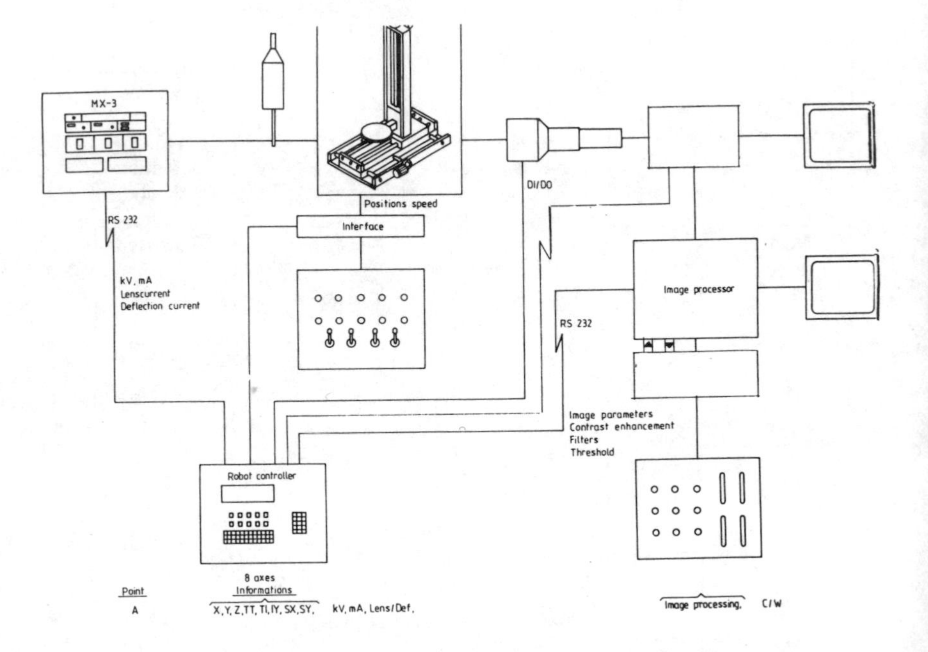

Fig. 3. A fully-robotized real-time X-ray system.

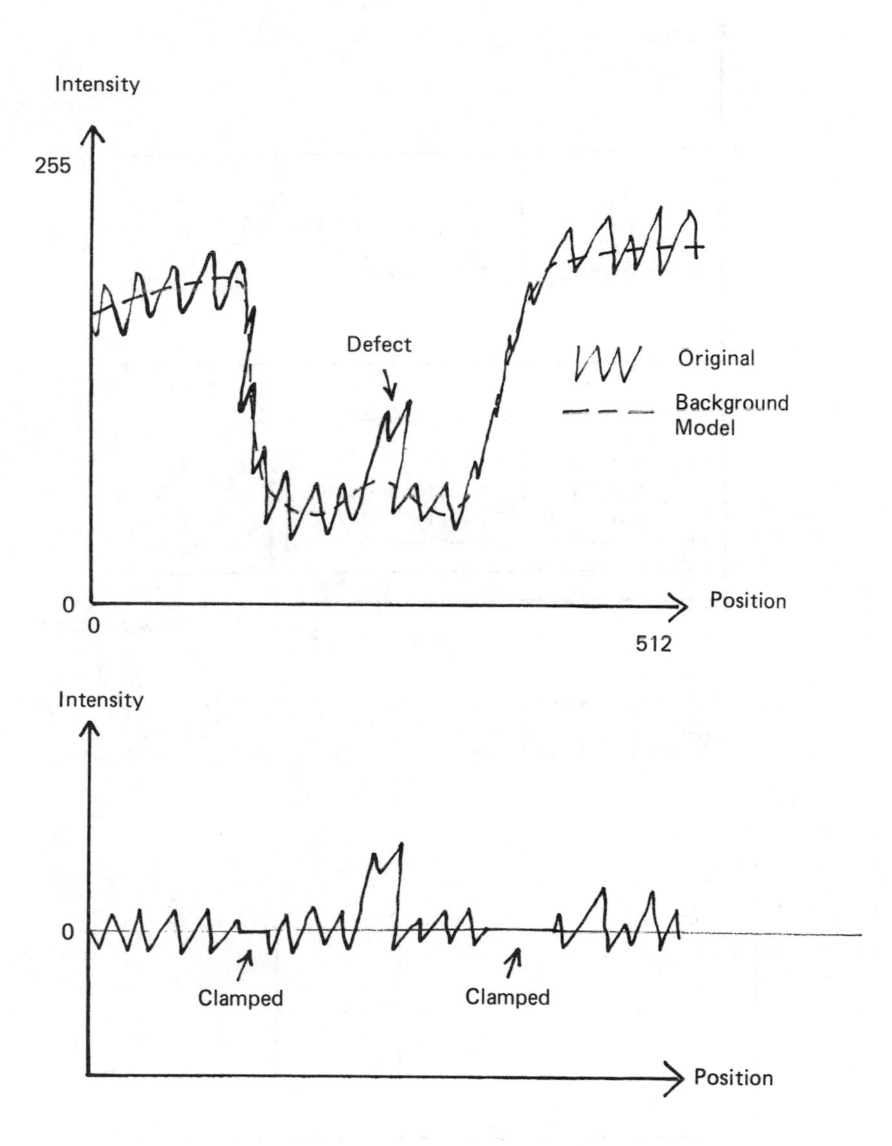

Fig.4. Background modelling and the difference image.

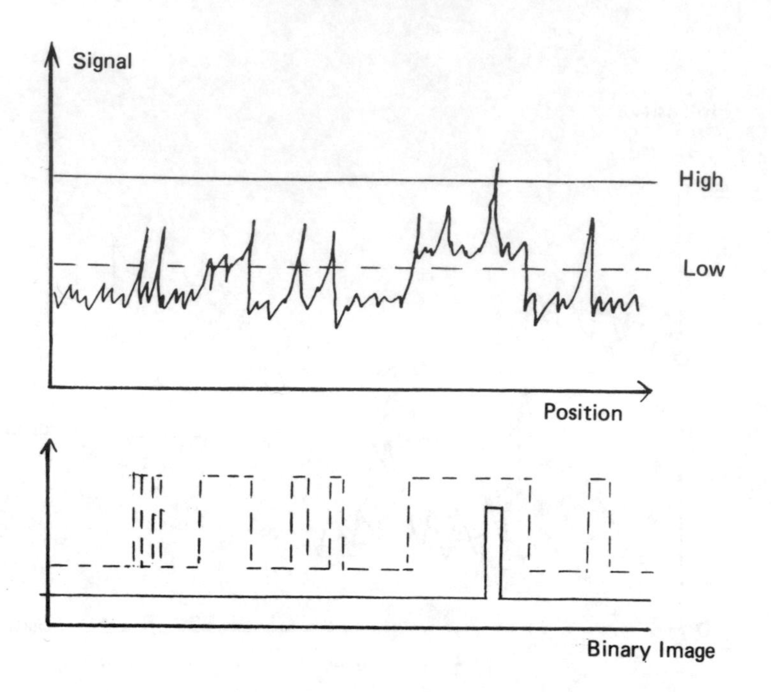

Fig.5. Single threshold. Too high settings will not give the required sensitivity. Too low a threshold will give too many false indications.

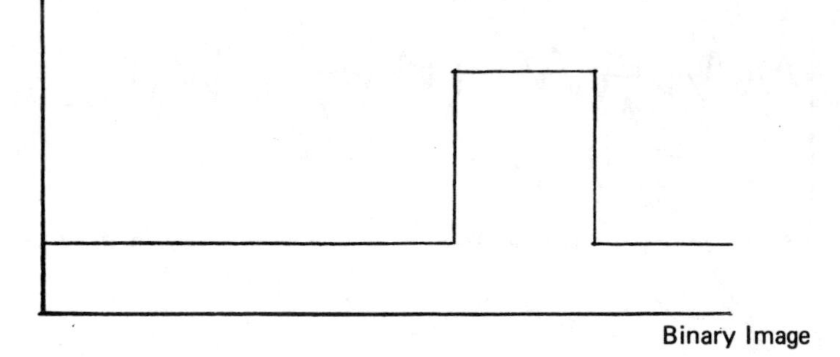

Fig.6. A combination of the two thresholds will give the correct size of the signal, but will still not detect the weak signals.

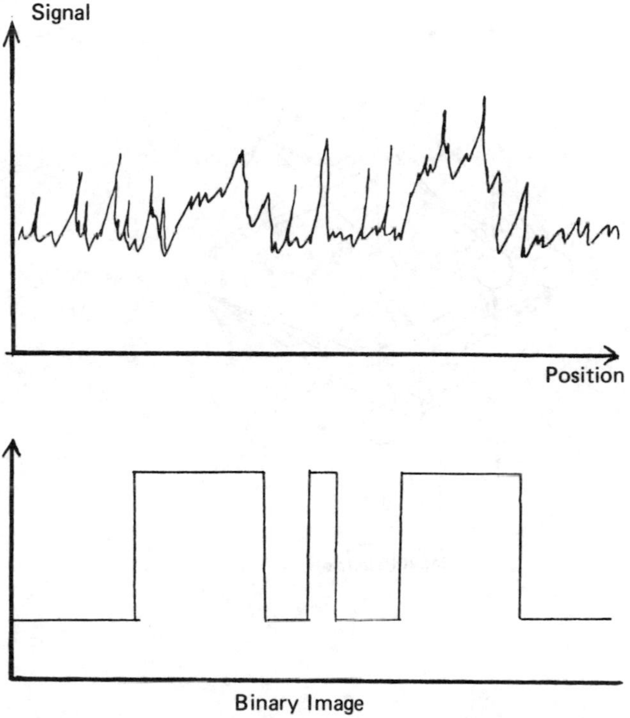

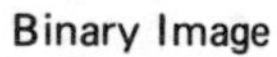

Fig.7. The simulated annealing will use all the information in the image to generate the best possible fit of a binary image to the original image.

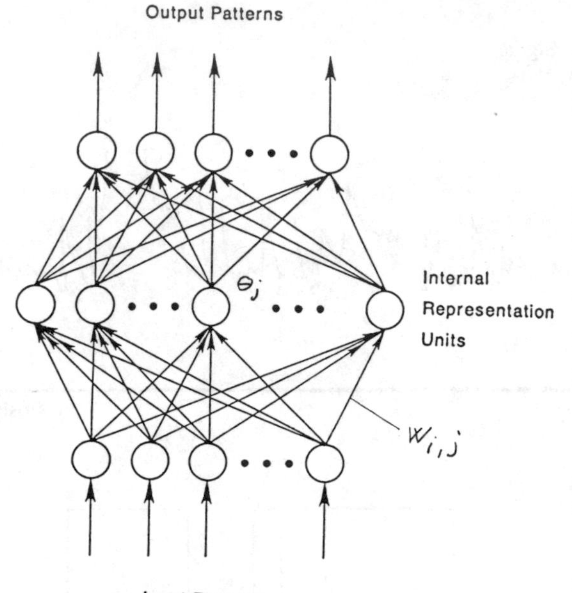

Fig.8. Neural Network model.

1. In the learning phase, the input is clamped to the training set and the result. The network is cooled to find the minimum energy. The weights w and the threshold 0 are determined to give the maximum fit to the learning set.
2. In the recognition phase, the input of the network is clamped to the set to be analysed and the network is cooled down using the weights and thresholds found under the learning phase. The output found at the lowest energy will be the most likely interpretation of the input.

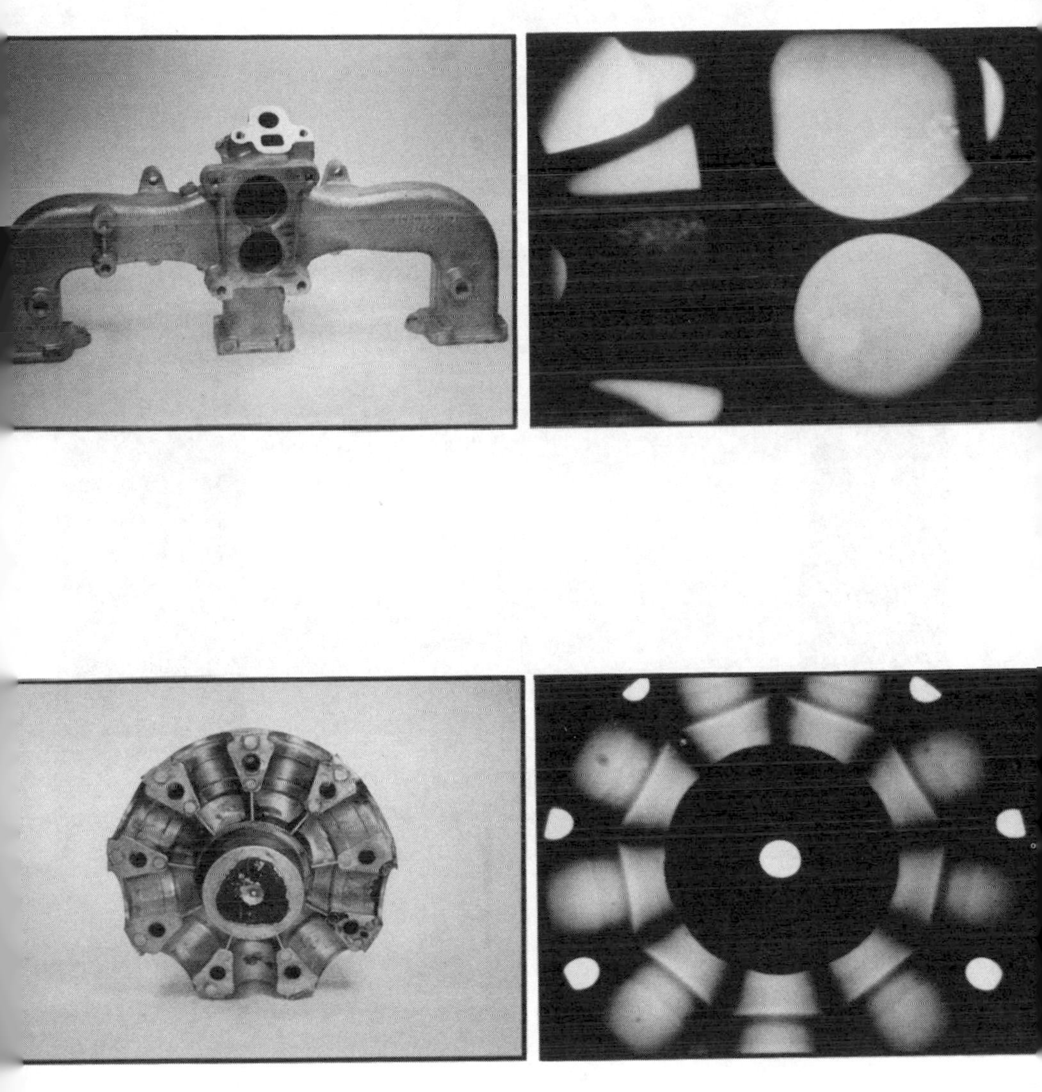

Fig. 9 Typical light alloy castings and assosiated real time images.

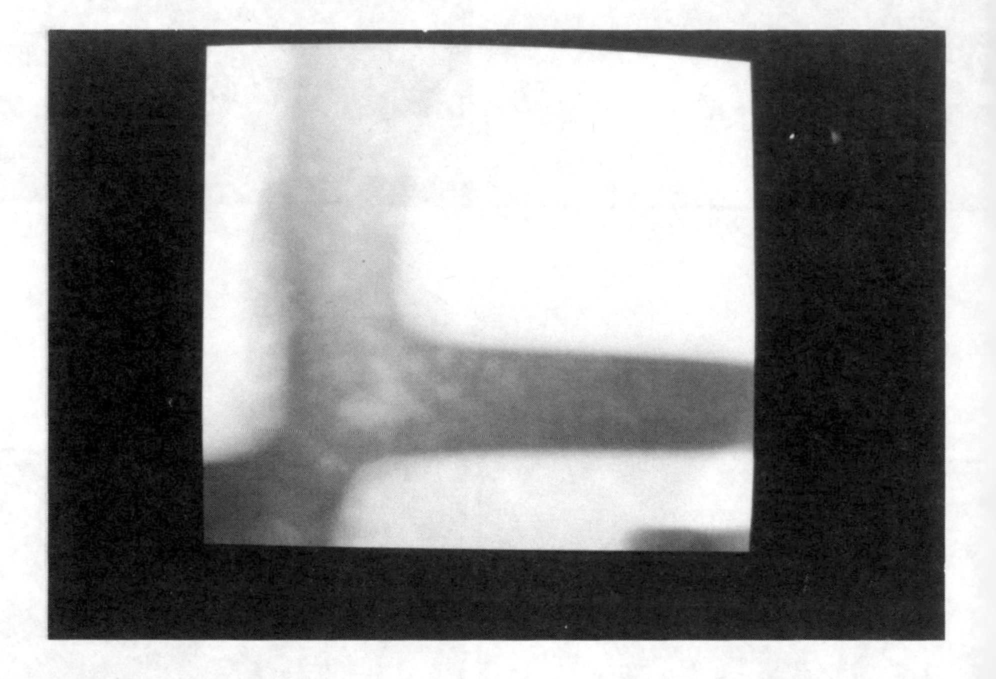

Fig. A1 Original X-ray image of light alloy casting. Integrated over 32 videoframes to reduce X-ray noise.

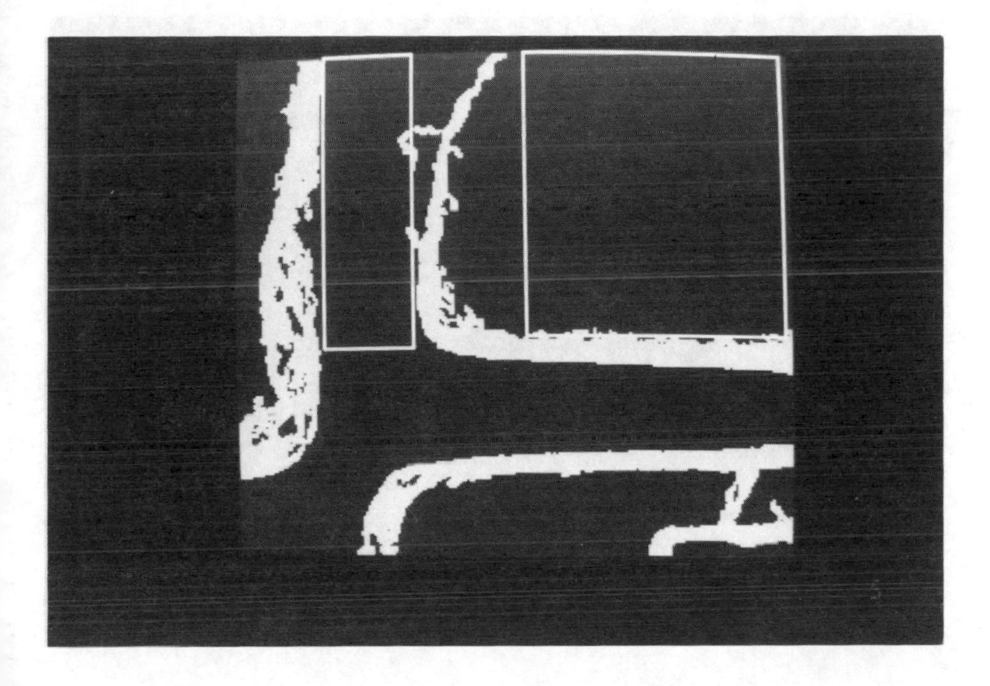

Fig. A2 Results of a combined edge detection and ROI determination. The ROI's have been determined from compressed information of a training set containing 12 castings. A simple Neural Network has been used.

Fig. A3 Difference image obtained by substracting the background model from the original image. The background model has been clamped to the edges as seen on figure A2.

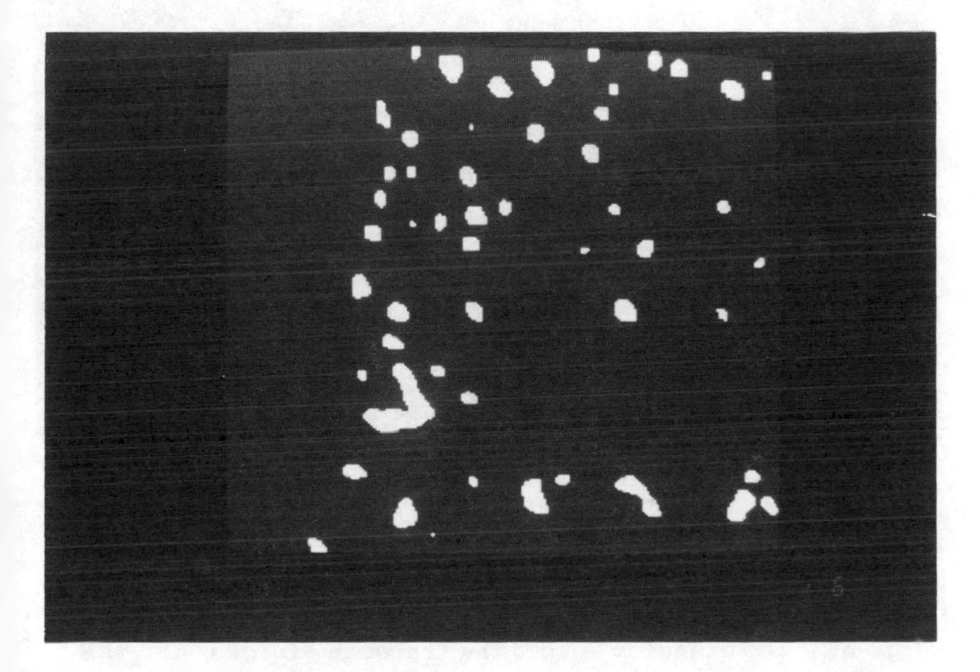

Fig. A4 Defect detection using simulated annealing for the optimal binarization.

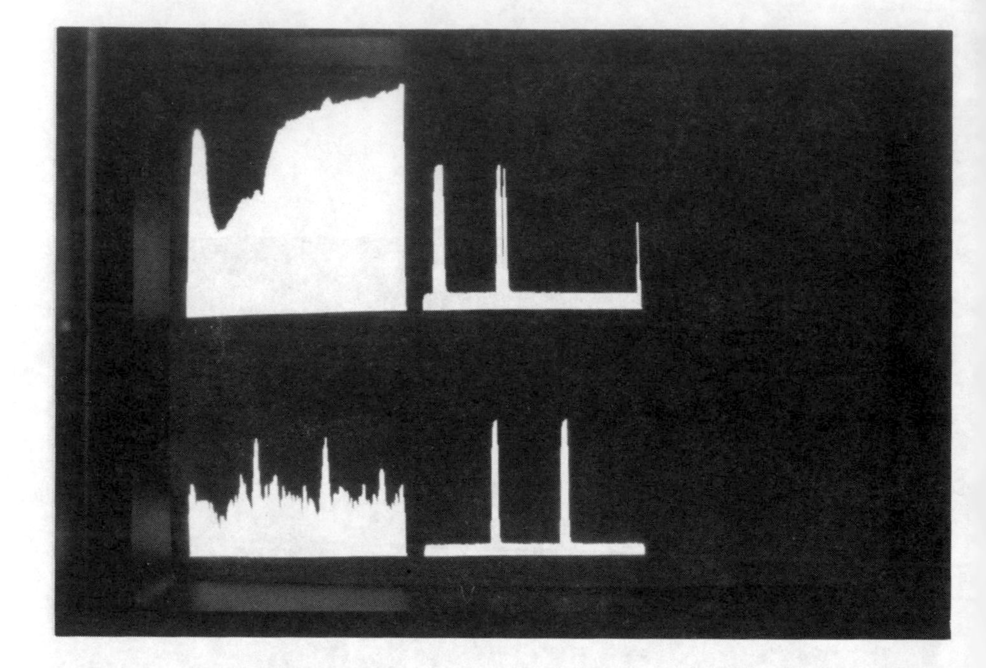

Figure A5.

Fig. A5 Intensity profiles through images in the different stages.

Upper left corner: profile through the original image.

Upper right corner: profile through the edge detected image.

Lower left corner: profile through the difference image.

Lower right corner: profile through the binary image.

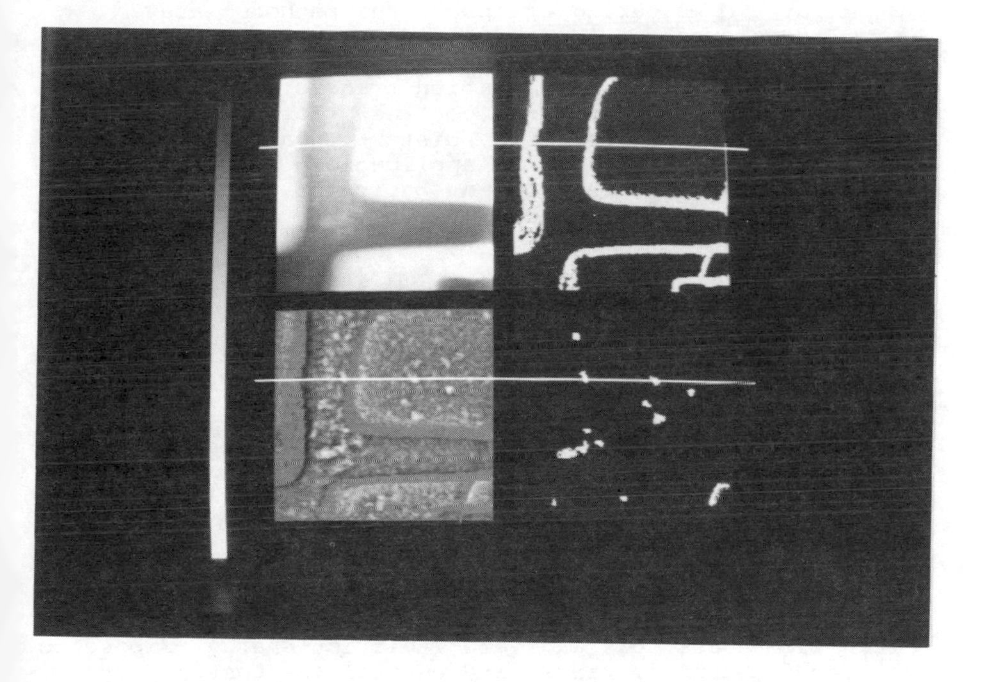

Fig. A6 Compressed view of the four stages of processing. The white lines indicate the positions in which the profiles are taken.

OBJECTIVE MEASUREMENTS ON IMAGE QUALITY OF X-RAY REAL-TIME IMAGING SYSTEMS

W DAUM AND H HEIDT

Transfer characteristic and image quality of an X-ray real-time imaging system are very important for the reliable detection of material defects. In order to determine these features in a quantitative and objective way, at BAM measuring equipment and methods were developed for these purposes. The development is based on common and objective image quality parameters like modulation transfer function, inherent unsharpness, contrast sensitivity, signal-to-noise-ratio, distortion and image uniformity. Practical applications show that the methods are a common basis for future system qualification.

INTRODUCTION

For the reliable and economic detection of material defects by means of X-rays, the transfer characteristic and image quality of the imaging system are very important. In the case of film radiography the properties governing the image quality are well understood[1]: contrast sensitivity, inherent unsharpness and graininess. Since the tolerances are small under good handling conditions, the standards for radiographic exposures give a straightforward-procedure: For a given wall thickness use a certain film-class, distance and radiation energy, expose to a specific density range, and control the contrast by image quality indicators (IQI). Then the radiographic image will give an approved detectability for defects.

For X-ray Real-Time Imaging systems (XRTI) the situation is completely different. At present, there exist three types of industrial XRTI systems with different construc-

Dipl.-Ing. W. Daum, Dr.-Ing. H. Heidt, Federal Institute for Materials Research and Testing (BAM), Berlin

tion features: 'open screen' type of equipment, X-ray image intensifier systems and linear array systems. The state of the art of these modern XRTI systems was improved in the last few years by better conversion screens, image intensifiers, TV-cameras and high resolution CCD-arrays, as well as the use of digital processors for image enhancement and image interpretation. But at present there exists no national or international standard which determines image quality parameters of XRTI systems and how they can be measured. Only some national guidelines were published, e. g. ASTM-Document E 1000-84 (1), BS 7009 : 1988 (2).

Till now the image quality of a complete XRTI system and the corresponding image quality parameters could only be determined by simple test patterns and a subjective visual evaluation of the monitor picture. In addition, there are additional and more complicated parameters in comparison to the film, like linearity, signal-to-noise ratio, homogeneity of the image, which cannot be determined by visual means. A lot of these parameters can be influenced by the producer and the user of the XRTI system, resulting in an adaption (or mismatch) to the specific testing problem. In order to overcome these problems and to determine the image quality parameters in a quantitative and objective way, at the Federal Institute for Materials Research and Testing (BAM) adaptable measuring methods and equipment were developed.

IMPORTANT IMAGE QUALITY PARAMETERS

Because there are many different construction types of XRTI systems with conversion screens, image intensifiers, TV-cameras and detector arrays, it is necessary to define common image quality parameters and principal methods how to measure them. In general, the radiation, which comes from the radiation source, penetrates the specimen. Interaction between the radiation and the matter of the specimen causes an absorption and scattering of the radiation. This means that in a plane behind the specimen the radiation shows a spatial modulated two-dimensional intensity distribution (radiation relief). Task of the XRTI system is to convert the radiation relief into an electrical signal (the video signal). Within the meaning of information theory, one can describe an XRTI system as an imaging device with the radiation relief as the input signal and the video signal as the output signal. With regard to image quality it is decisive that the information content of the radiation relief is represented in the video signal with a minimum loss of information. From this point-of-view it is possible to describe the complete XRTI system in terms of information theory and to use the radiation relief and the video signal as standard interfaces for system measurements. This has also the advantage that measurements are possible under industrial conditions without dismounting the whole system or system parts. This means that for quantitative measurements the specimen can be replaced by an artificial test indicator, and performance measurement can be done at the video output signal (Fig. 1).

On basis of these principal measuring methods, it is possible to characterize and to compare the image quality of industrial XRTI systems with the following parameters:

Modulation Transfer Function (MTF)

Spatial resolution is usually described by the modulation transfer function. It specifies the relative frequency response of the imaging system to a sinusoidal, spatially modulated radiation relief, which represents defects of different sizes. At low spatial frequencies (large defects) a density change will be transferred with a modulation of 1 (100 %); that means no loss in contrast. Going to higher spatial frequencies, for smaller density changes of the same radiation contrast, the modulation will be lower because of system limitations. An XRTI system is better for small detail detection if the part of the MTF curve having a modulation of 1 (100%) is longer. Measurement ot MTF can be performed with a sharp edge and additional signal processing or - easier - with a repeating bar-pattern of different spatial frequencies. From the video output signal across the bar-pattern one can determine the modulation depth for each spatial frequency, which gives one point on the MTF-curve (Fig. 2).

Limiting Resolution

The limiting resolution of an XRTI system is defined as being the highest spatial frequency of a pattern that can be detected by the eye. It corresponds to a modulation on the order of 5 % for the MTF. The limiting resolution can be determined from the MTF-curve or it can also be measured separately with the same test pattern.

Inherent Unsharpness

The accurate parameter to describe the spatial resolution of an XRTI system is only the MTF because this parameter takes the non-linearity of the transfer characteristic into consideration. But for practical application (e. g. calculation of the optimal geometric magnification) it is often suitable to know in addition the value of inherent unsharpness. Two methods of measurement are applied in radiography: the method of Klasens and the visual evaluation of double wire IQI's. Klasens' method evaluates the response signal from a high contrast step (Fig. 3). From the line crossing two defined levels of the video output signal one can determine the inherent unsharpness under the condition that the geometric unsharpness is negligible. Because with double wire IQI's it is only possible to determine the unsharpness in discrete values, it is not suitable for measurement. But it is sufficient for quick visual control of system stability.

Contrast Sensitivity

Besides the spatial resolution it is very important to measure the smallest radiation contrast which is transferred by an XRTI system. For practical application the smallest transferred radiation contrast itself is not of such interest. More significant is to measure the smallest wall thickness change in a specific material which can be detected with an XRTI system for a given wall thickness, under pre-defined radiation conditions. The ratio of the wall thickness change to the wall thickness gives then the value for 'contrast- or thickness sensitivity'. In industrial radiography there are different types (step- and wire IQI's) of test pattern in use to simulate a defined wall thickness change. For correct measurement of contrast sensitivity it is very important, that the size of the test pattern is large enough so that there is no loss in contrast because of the MTF. To overcome this problem it is recommended to use step IQI's (e. g. CERL-A-IQI) instead of wire IQI's. From the video output signal across the step-IQI one can determine the thinnest transmitted plate and calculate the contrast sensitivity. It is defined that the thinnest transmitted plate must have a signal-to-noise ratio larger than 2 in the video output signal.

Signal-to-Noise Ratio

The signal-to-noise ratio indicates the influence of numerous system parameters (e. g. thermal and electronic effects) on the impression of noise which can rise from an homogeneous image. Under the assumption that there is no automatic gain control within the system, then the maximum possible signal-to-noise ratio is defined by the maximum output amplitude divided by the mean amplitude of the dark current noise. If there is an automatic gain control, then the signal-to-noise ratio must be determined for different gain stages.

Distortion and Image Uniformity

Local geometric distortion and image uniformity are further image quality parameters which have an influence on defect representation in the final image. Local distortion can be measured by evaluating the image of a small lead disc, which is positioned in front of the XRTI system. A measurement of image uniformity is performed through the detection of maximum and minimum video output amplitude of an uniformity irradiated XRTI system.

RESULTS OF MEASUREMENT

In order to determine the described image quality parameters in a quantitative and objective way, at the BAM measuring equipment for this purpose was developed. The measuring equipment consists of three main components (Fig. 1):

- host computer with peripherals,
- digital image processing system with special soft- and hardware for radiographic purposes,
- high resolution digital video measuring oscilloscope with fast signal processing facilities.

For practical application, the developed measuring methods in combination with the measuring equipment, offers a lot of different facilities:

- measurement and evaluation of the image quality of installed XRTI systems,
- image quality check of an XRTI system with regard to technical specifications,
- objective and quantitative comparison of image quality of XRTI systems from various manufacturers and with

different construction features, in order to find the best system for a special inspection problem,
- specific improvement of the image quality for a specific inspection problem in co-operation with manufacturer and customer.

For example, with the measuring equipment, the image quality of 6 prototypes of modern XRTI systems for weld inspection was measured under normalized conditions. All systems were based on X-ray image intensifiers, the mostly used type of equipment in industrial real-time radiographic inspection of welds.

Between the systems remarkable image quality differences occur. This applies especially to the spatial resolution. Figure 4 shows the tolerance range of the modulation transfer function. For example the modulation for a spatial resolution of 1 lp/mm varies in a range of 20 % to 72 % by an energy of 95 kV and 22 mm Al radiation filtering.

These differences can also be recognized at the limiting resolution (Fig. 5a). The limiting resolution of a radioscopic system is defined as being the highest spatial frequency of a pattern that can be detected at the output signal of the system. For large field size it varies between 1.6 lp/mm to 2.0 lp/mm and for small field size between 2.5 lp/mm to 3.4 lp/mm.

Contrast sensitivity of a radioscopic system is an important image quality parameter for the detection of small wall thickness changes. It was measured in a wall thickness range of 2 mm to 10 mm steel with a CERL-A-IQI. For example the wall thickness change with t_{Fe} = 6 mm and Δt = 2.16 % was detected from the different radioscopic systems with an output signal amplitude of 3.4 % to 6.5 % of the maximum amplitude. For these measurements the feature of image integration was used to improve the signal-to-noise ratio.

Finally, local distortion and image uniformity of the 6 radioscopic systems were measured. Both image quality parameters show a range of values between 30 % and 10 % at outer image regions for the different systems (Fig. 5b and Fig. 5c).

CONCLUSIONS

The given examples and results show that XRTI systems are much more complex and difficult to characterize with regard to image quality compared to the traditional radiography. But by means of information theory and a special measuring equipment it is possible to characterize the image quality with objective and quantitative parameters.

REFERENCES

(1) Standard guide for Radiologic Real-Time Imaging, ASTM-Document Nr. E 1000-84
(2) British Standard Guide to Application of real-time radiography to weld inspection, BS 7009 : 1988

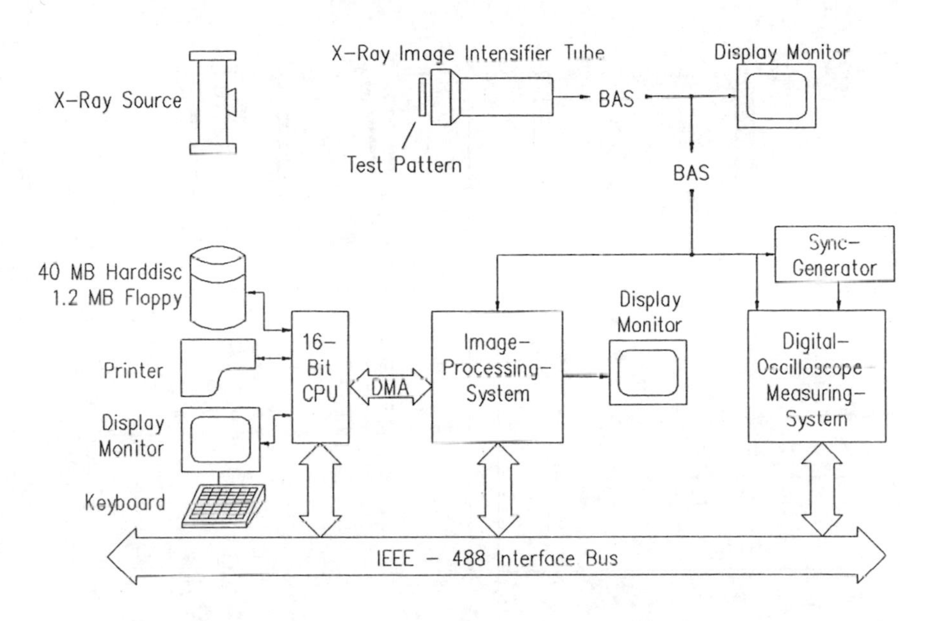

Fig 1 Measuring equipment and experimental set-up

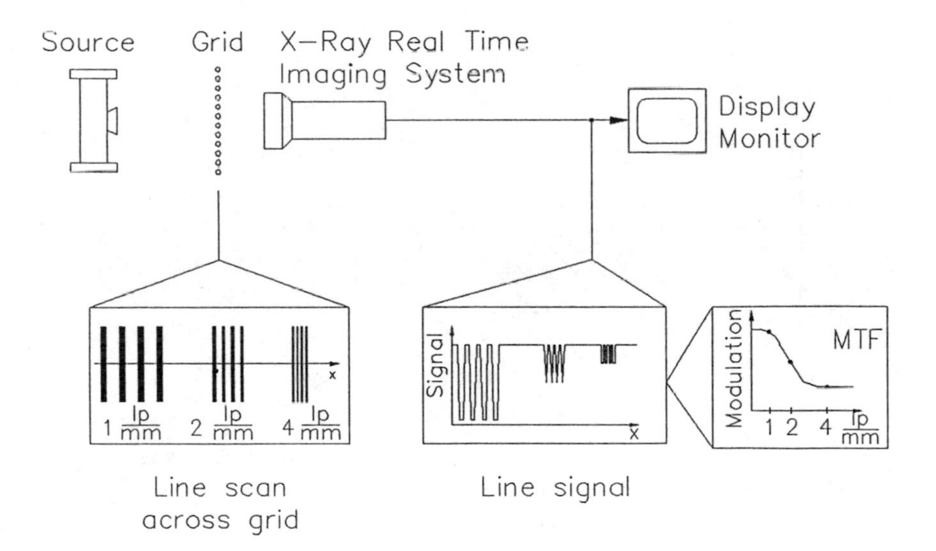

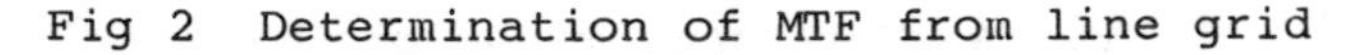
Fig 2 Determination of MTF from line grid

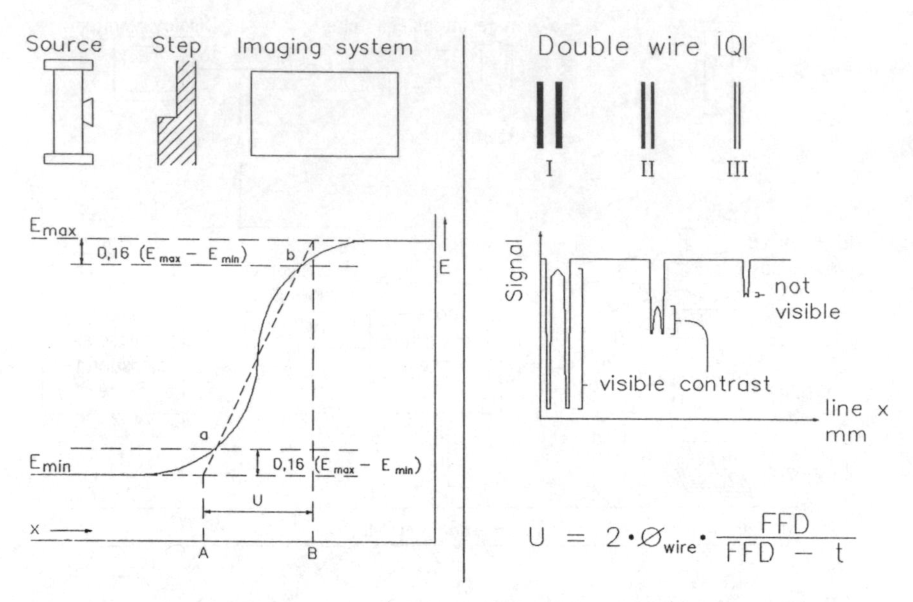

Fig 3 Determination of inherent unsharpness

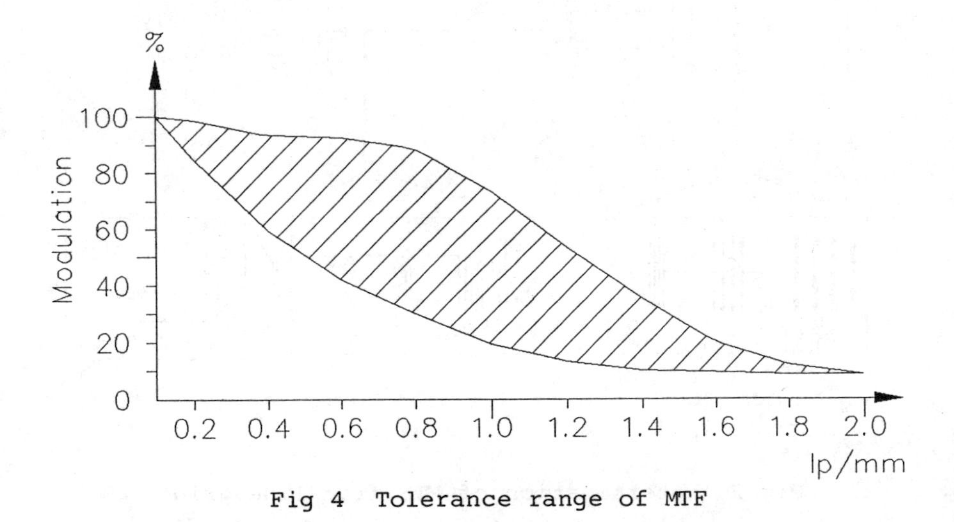

Fig 4 Tolerance range of MTF

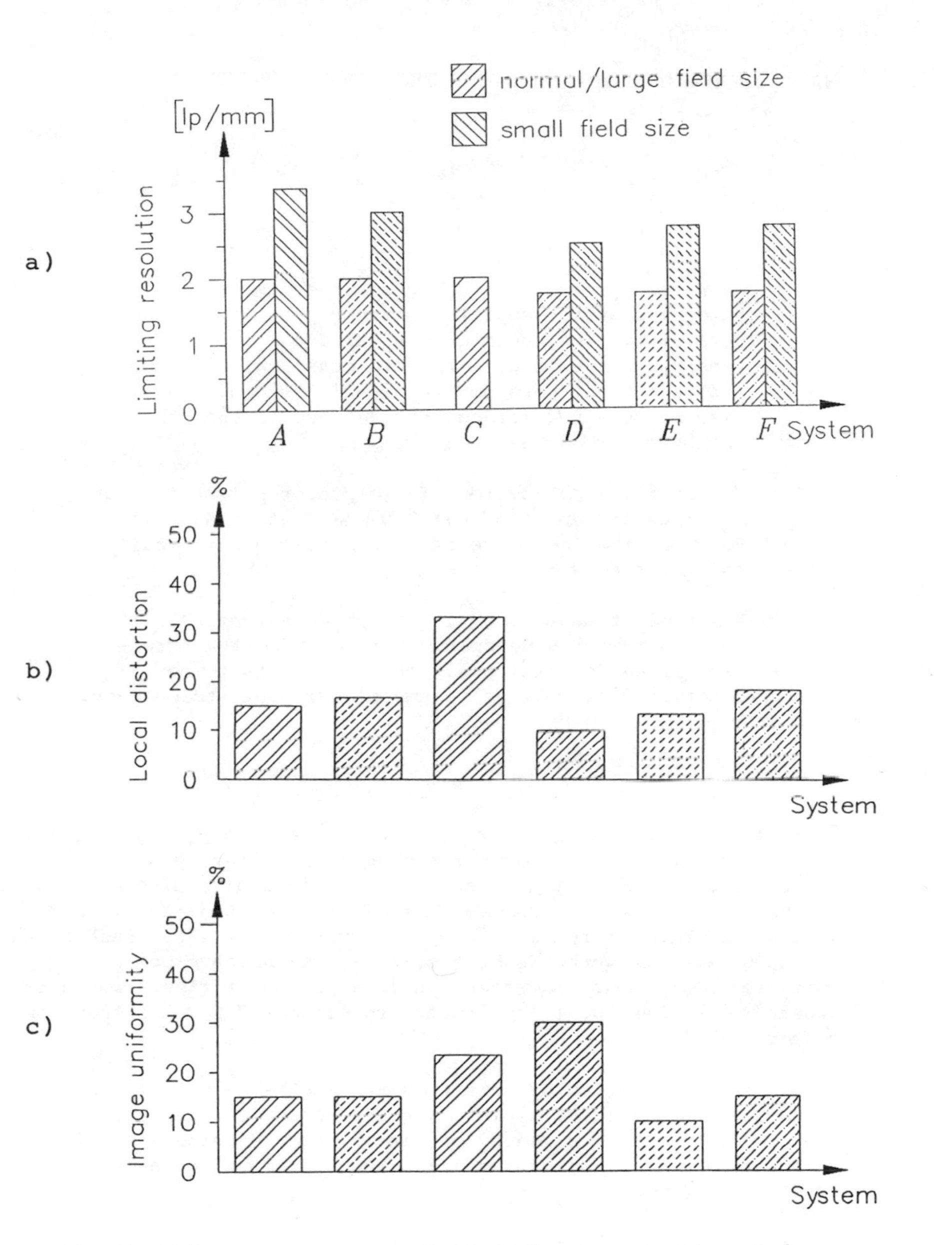

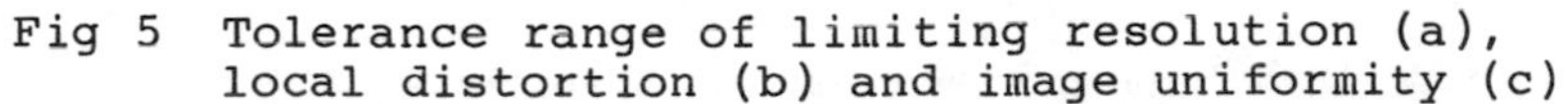
Fig 5 Tolerance range of limiting resolution (a), local distortion (b) and image uniformity (c)

NOVEL THREE-DIMENSIONAL IMAGING TECHNIQUES APPLIED TO X-RAYS

M ROBINSON

An x-ray system having a full three-dimensional (ie binocular stereoscopic) imaging capability has been developed. The technique is based on linear array sensors. As well as a three-dimensional image, both left and right perspective two-dimensional views can also be obtained for one single pass through the machine.

The initial application of the prototype was in high security screening of cargo by HM Customs & Excise. However, the technique is also applicable to medical and NDT type work.

A method of measuring x, y and z coordinates in the image has been developed. This enables the three-dimensional spatial positions of objects to be determined as well as volume measurements to be made.

INTRODUCTION

Work has been carried out for a number of years on the development of three-dimensional (ie binocular stereoscopic) imaging systems based on closed circuit television cameras. The main application areas of this technology have been in remote control vehicle guidance (1) and manipulator arm control in hazardous environments (2). Much of the attention in this work has been directed to the development of suitable image sensor packages. Over a period of time, considerable expertise has been built up in the production of novel stereoscopic sensors (3).

As a natural extension of this work and as the result of a requirement by HM Customs & Excise, a prototype stereoscopic x-ray system was produced (4). This was based on linear array detectors and is effectively a three-dimensional imaging system using one-dimensional sensors.

Dr M Robinson, InDepth Systems Ltd, Nottingham and
Trent Polytechnic, Nottingham

In order to put into context the new three-dimensional x-ray system, a brief description of the way in which humans perceive the three-dimensional world will be presented. Also, information concerning developments in stereoscopic television systems will be given since the three-dimensional x-ray system developed presents the images on a video display.

THREE-DIMENSIONAL HUMAN VISION

Human beings determine the positions of objects in the real, three-dimensional world via a variety of distinctly different depth cues. Some of these are purely psychological such as interposition, linear perspective and the effects of shades and shadows. In general, it is relatively easy to disguise the reality of a situation when only psychological cues are used. However, a number of powerful physiological depth cues are also available to enable us to determine the relative positions of objects in space.

Prominent amongst these are the linked binocular mechanisms of convergence and accommodation and also monocular movement parallax. The most powerful cue employed by humans over a short range, however, is that of binocular parallax. Simply put, this means that objects at different distances from an observer will have images on each retina having different relative lateral separations. The eyes are capable of discriminating very small variations in this parallax information and translating them into depth information.

THREE-DIMENSIONAL TELEVISION

In a normal television display only a certain proportion of the total number of depth cues are available to an observer. Some are missing due to image quality degradation inherent in video displays and some due to the system's monocularity. For example, interposition is a very strong depth cue in normal television but texture gradient is almost non-existent. There are, however, sufficient reinforcing depth cues to provide an acceptable entertainment medium. Many of these will of course be considerably enhanced with the advent of the high definition television standard.

When a human observer is linked to a scene by a normal closed circuit television system, the most significant piece of information relating to spatial awareness, ie the parallax which arises from binocular vision, is not contained in the display. Consequently, judgements relating to spatial positions and movements made from such a scene are very often unreliable. These problems are exaggerated when complex scenes are to be interpreted or manipulative tasks are to be performed.

The solution is to employ a three-dimensional display system. Historically, a disproportionate amount of effort has been expended on a variety of methods for viewing three-dimensional television displays whilst relatively little attention has been given to the development of suitable stereo-sensors. Without a means of correctly extracting visual information from the real world and then presenting it in true registration, none of the various viewing methods will provide acceptable stereoscopic images. This premise is equally true for three-dimensional x-ray images. What is required, therefore, is a thorough knowledge of stereoscopic sensing before usable three-dimensional imaging systems can be produced.

THREE-DIMENSIONAL COMPUTER GRAPHICS

The computer graphics fraternity have in recent years advertised their products as having a three-dimensional capability. In most instances this has not meant a binocular stereoscopic display. There is now effectively a crisis of terminology because of this. A computer-aided design (CAD) system having a so called three-dimensional display usually means that certain psychological depth cues such as linear perspective and interposition have been introduced. Even with the addition of the effects of shading and shadows, the displays contain fewer three-dimensional depth cues than a broadcast television signal. It is inconceivable that the BBC or IBA would claim that their current transmissions are three-dimensional.

A few notable exceptions exist, however, where CAD systems do produce full stereoscopic images, but the step-up in computing power necessary to manipulate such an image from that required for a pseudo three-dimensional image is quite considerable.

Caution must be exercised therefore when claims of three-dimensional capability are made to establish exactly what combination of depth cues are being presented.

THREE-DIMENSIONAL X-RAY IMAGES

X-ray imaging in a variety of forms has become a standard analytical technique in many diverse fields. Prominent amongst these are the multiplicity of uses employed by the medical profession and also the many applications of quality control and assessment used in industrial non-destructive testing (NDT).

In all of these situations, except for a few specific laboratory set-ups, the images produced are two-dimensional in nature. Interpretation of these images, whether from photographic film or more recently from a variety of display monitors, is based solely on flat image shape and grey level information related to the penetration of the particular range of x-ray energies being employed.

X-ray imagery is unique in that many of the usual powerful three-dimensional depth cues that humans are able to extract from two-dimensional images are missing. Examples of these cues are interposition, the effects of shading and shadows, texture gradient, and to some extent, linear perspective. Almost all of these cues and others are available, for example, in an ordinary photograph. The difference is that a photograph is produced by reflected light whereas an x-ray picture is derived from transmitted radiation. This consequent loss of depth cues can, and does, cause serious ambiguities to arise in the interpretation of complex images.

Attempts to overcome this inherent problem with x-ray imagery have in the past involved using bulky equipment, employing tedious operating procedures, and have usually been time-consuming and expensive.

For example, stereoscopic pairs of x-ray plates have been produced by the medical world in the past. They usually require the patient to be motionless for some considerable time whilst each perspective view (left and right) is taken sequentially. Further delays occur before the images may be viewed, usually via a stereoscope, and should any three-dimensional measurements be required, then the use of some kind of stereo-comparator would be necessary.

Pseudo three-dimensional x-ray images are currently derived from standard computer tomography (CT) scanners. These enhanced images are not readily available since they are very computer intensive and consequently costly in their production. They involve the introduction of a number of depth cues into the images by "computer-aided joining together" of a number of CT scan slices. This is obviously an approximation since any irregularity between adjacent slices cannot be seen.

A major departure from all these techniques has been the development of a true three-dimensional (ie binocular stereoscopic) x-ray system based on linear arrays. Historically, this type of detector was of such coarse resolution that its use in an NDT or medical context was inappropriate. Recently, however, high resolution linear arrays (5) capable of resolving to a fraction of a millimetre have become available. A further bonus is that the sensitivity of this type of detector is such that they now compare very favourably with photographic film.

In the normal two-dimensional mode of operation a linear array x-ray system operates as follows. A thin collimated curtain of x-rays is derived from an x-ray source and targeted onto the linear detector. Relative movement now between the object to be imaged and the x-ray beam causes an image to be built up when the linear detector electronically scans in synchronism with the speed of object movement. The digitised image information which is captured is then loaded directly into a frame store.

The three-dimensional version of this technique can take two forms, either of which are able to aquire a left and right perspective view of the object under inspection during one single pass.

In one configuration two linear detectors and two x-ray sources are used. A more elegant technique, however, is to use only one x-ray source and to derive two collimated beams from it; again two linear detectors are required. The amount of depth perceived in the stereoscopic image by an observer will be controlled to some extent, but not entirely, by this x-ray beam/linear detector array geometry.

Solutions to the problems of manipulating the x-ray intensity information received from two sensors, which are usually scanning different parts of the same object at the same time, and of designing the x-ray beam geometry such that successful reconstruction of real three-dimensional image of an object is possible, have been derived.

VIEWING THE IMAGE

The method selected for observing the three-dimensional x-ray image is known variously as the time division or field sequential type of display. The technique takes advantage of the interlace facility used in normal video displays and the short retention memory capability to visual stimuli of the human eye/brain combination. Left and right perspective views are displayed sequentially on the monitor screen whilst the observer views that image through liquid crystal glasses which are switching, transparent and opaque in synchronism with the display. The speed of switching is at twice the standard video rate and so a solid three-dimensional image whithout any perceived flicker is observed. An alternative method used has been to place an active liquid crystal plate in front of the monitor screen and then to view the image using polaroid (circularly polarized) glasses. The left or right two-dimensional image can also be viewed in this way.

Two interesting and useful phenomena have been observed. Firstly, since normal x-ray images contain very few, if any, depth cues,it has been shown that by altering the phase of the viewing glasses (ie presenting left eye information to the right eye and vice versa) a three- dimensional view of the object from the opposite side may also be obtained. Quite simply one may observe the three-dimensional image of the object from the position of the x-ray source, or alternatively the position of the linear detectors. This is possible since the only depth cue being presented is binocular parallax. This technique would not work with a stereoscopic image derived from television cameras since other conflicting depth cues would also be presented.

A second useful artefact of the images is an apparent pseudo-movement parallax. Normally, movement parallax manifests itself as an increased movement of foreground object relative to background when an observer moves laterally with respect to a scene. In stereoscopic images an "apparent" greater movement of the background occurs. This can be used as a powerful depth cue especially for complex images. Other effects are also possible such as electronically "shifting" the image in and out of the monitor screen. This technique ensures that the complete stereoscopic depth of field is utilised.

MEASUREMENT IN STEREOSCOPIC DISPLAYS

A technique has been developed for measuring x, y and z coordinates in stereoscopic video images (6). The method uses measuring markers inserted into the left and right perspective views. The disparity information obtained in this way of conjugate points in each image is a measure of the z-coordinate. It is necessary to calibrate the system initially in order to eliminate distortions in the display due to geometrical misalignment, the electron-optics of the display and the inherent distortion due to point source illumination in an x-ray image.

The calibration technique (7) is a derivation of tried and tested methods used in standard close-range photogrammetry.

Each individual pixel separation in a display between left and right conjugate pionts gives rise to an individually resolvable depth plane. In a correctly constructed image this number could be quite large. Consequently, images are produced with a considerably higher density of depth planes than would be obtained from the normal use of a CT scanner. This occurs in a matter of a few seconds without the need for expensive computing equipment.

Work is under way to develop image enhancement and analysis routines specifically for three-dimensional x-ray images. Initial results show considerable potential for the future.

SUMMARY

Some important advantages of this new technology are considered to be as follows:

(i) speed of image acquisition;
(ii) immediate display of two-dimensional or true three-dimensional image;
(iii) high level of image information;
(iv) rapid three-dimensional coordinate measurement facility giving positional and volumetric information;
(v) low x-ray dose for image acquisition;
(vi) immediate application of image enhancement and analysis routines;
(vii) provision of hard copy records of images if required.

REFERENCES

(1) Robinson, M, "Remote control vehicle guidance using stereoscopic displays", Proc. US Human Factors, Vol 28, 1984, p 809.

(2) Robinson, M, "Three-dimensional vision for bomb disposal", 8th Int Conf Special Equipment for the Police, INTERPOL HQ Paris, 1983.

(3) Robinson, M, Shuttleworth, P, "The development of stereoscopic vision systems for use in hazardous environments", Proc. Int. Symp. Teleoperation and Control, The Ergonomics Society, 1988, pp 191-195.

(4) Robinson, M, "Three-dimensional visual screening system", British Patent Application No 8623196, Sept 1986.

(5) Munier, B and others, "Solid state 1024 pixel linear x-ray detector", SPIE Vol 809, Scanning Imaging Technology, 1987, pp 80-84.

(6) Robinson, M, Sood, SC, "Calibration and depth resolution of a stereoscopic video display", SPIE Vol 402, 1983, pp 162-165.

(7) Robinson, M, Ariyaeeinia, AM, "An active coordinate imaging system for robot vision", SPIE Vol 657, Applications of Artificial Intelligence, 1986, pp 144-151.

THE DEVELOPMENT OF SCORPIO AS A COMMERCIAL PRODUCT

IJ SHELLARD, C BAXTER, AT JONES

1. Introduction

SCORPIO is an inspection system used in precision casting facilities to measure the orientation of the crystal axes with respect to the design axes within single-crystal turbine components.

The system is used in the production environment (rather than in a laboratory) and, as such, is operated either by production quality control personnel or, in the latest developments, totally robotically.

This paper describes the factors which created the need for SCORPIO and also the history of its technical development, but concentrates on the effect that the decision for Rolls-Royce plc to market the product commercially has had on the specification and the manner in which the project has progressed.

2. The Need for SCORPIO

In recent years, whilst the development of new materials, such as composites, has had a major effect on the design of low-temperature structural components in aeroengines, the main factors in the turbine itself have been improvements and innovations in the manufacturing process. (Ref 1)

The manufacture of turbine blades as single crystals, ie effectively without grain boundaries, offers considerable improvements in performance but these are dependent upon the orientation of the crystal axes with respect to the principle load directions. For example, the most common orientation (aligning the <001> crystal axis of the cubic structured alloy with the principal stress direction (Fig 1)) offers improved

SHELLARD - ROLLS-ROYCE BUSINESS VENTURES LIMITED
BAXTER AND JONES - ROLLS-ROYCE plc

life at high temperature, which gives the designer the opportunity to increase turbine temperatures (and, hence, fuel efficiency) or to increase the interval between engine overhauls. By contrast, an alternative orientation (aligning the crystal <111> direction with the blade axis) offers increased ultimate tensile strength, which has application where weight, rather than life, is the main criterion.

Clearly, it is essential that a method exists for ensuring that the crystal orientation of production components is as designed, and this has led to a mandatory requirement to measure the orientation of each individual single crystal blade manufactured.

The original method for measuring the orientation made use of back-reflection Laue X-ray diffraction. In this technique, a polychromatic X-ray beam (typically using a Molybdenum or tungsten tube with an excitation potential of 40kv to 50 kv and a tube current of around 20mA) impinges onto the component, which is held in a precision fixture (Fig 2).

The back-reflected diffraction pattern is recorded on X-ray-sensitive film, which may be either a wet film negative or a Polaroid positive (Fig 3).

A trained operative then analyses the pattern by hand, using a Greninger chart.

This method is unsuited to production use for a number of reasons: Firstly the analysis is time consuming - particularly as there is an increasing need to measure the positions of 3 major axes of the crystal, which can take many minutes - and requires a highly skilled inspector. Secondly, the film itself is expensive, requires special storage and also needs exposure times of perhaps 30 seconds to 2½ minutes. In low-volume production, the analysis is the major factor but in the volumes now being produced at Rolls-Royce plc and other leading single-crystal blademakers, the film costs are themselves unacceptable.

Rolls-Royce plc therefore recognised, in the late 1970's, the need to develop an automated technique for measuring crystal orientation which removed both the need for film and for skilled operators.

The SCORPIO programme which resulted was aimed at developing a fully robotic system for this inspection, but was also constructed to achieve a working film-free system using production operators at the earliest possible date. This first SCORPIO would also be designed such that it became a part of the final robotic system rather than being superseded as development progressed.

3. The Development of SCORPIO Prior to Commercial Sales

The first stage of the project was to determine the technique on which the development would be based. Although the back-reflection Laue diffraction method was well established, there were other methods which could potentially be used to measure orientation, including optical techniques and ultrasonics. After investigation, however, it was concluded that the Laue technique, as well as being proven in practice, offered the greatest flexibility and the best opportunity for automation. Development of a system based on this method therefore began around 1980.

The two main elements of the system - the real-time X-ray diffraction detector and the analysis technique - proceeded in parallel.

In the early stages of the development of the analysis technique the diffraction pattern was captured by viewing a back-lit negative with a television camera and taking the video output into an image analysis system. This method was chosen in preference to, for example, using a stylus on a digitising tablet because of its compatibility with the type of detector being developed.

It was essential that the operator-controlled version of the system would give accurate, repeatable analyses in a minimum time. The key to this was to make the operating procedure simple to use but to make the entry of incorrect data difficult.

After tests, a pattern-matching technique was selected. In this, the Laue pattern is captured on the image analysis system, and the operator overlays a computer-generated spot on the centre of symmetry of the detected pattern. At this point a full Laue pattern is generated by the computer (Fig 4). The operator overlays this pattern on the detected pattern. When a match is achieved, the system records the orientation.

It was found that this technique met the objectives in that the operator could clearly and simply distinguish each 'arm' of the pattern, which is a problem with systems which mark individual spots. Furthermore, repeatability of results was also better than with 'spot marking' techniques, because the operator 'averages' the match over the whole detected pattern, thereby eliminating errors where detected spots are indistinct.

This technique was first applied in 1982.

After evaluating a range of possible detector options, it was decided to concentrate on a high sensitivity X-ray television system as this technology had already been demonstrated by Professor Arndt at Cambridge University.

The detector was developed jointly by Rolls-Royce plc and JD Jackson Electronics of Newark with an emphasis on engineering the unit for use in a production facility. Hence the construction is as rugged as possible given the nature of real-time detectors, and special fixturing was designed to maintain the correct alignment of the X-ray beam, the specimen and the detector.

The principle of operation of the detector is as follows: An X-ray sensitive phosphor converts the incident back scattered X-rays to light. This phosphor is deposited onto a removable fibre-optic faceplate which is in turn optically coupled to an image intensifier tube. The faceplate is included to ease repair in the event that the phospor becomes damaged, although outer protective covers minimise this possibility.

The output window of the image intensifier is coupled, via another fibre-optic component, to a SIT camera whose video output is displayed on a high resolution monitor.

Development of the detector was also completed in 1982 and the next phase of the development was to integrate the detector with the analysis system.

It was essential that the most relevant part of the diffraction pattern was detected for analysis. In the film method, this is achieved by positioning the film symmetrically about the X-ray collimator and aligning the specimen axis of interest with the X-ray beam (Fig 2).

Clearly this was not possible when the film was replaced by a television based detector, so an alternative geometry had to be derived which achieved similar results. It was found that simply moving the detector to the side, leaving the specimen positioned as before, was inadequate because the desired part of the X-ray pattern was no longer recorded. However, by re-positioning the specimen such that the axis of interest bisected the angle between the X-ray beam and the detector centre line, it was found that a pattern similar to a conventional back-reflection pattern could be obtained. Whilst the change in geometry introduced a slight change in the shape of the pattern, it was found that the new patterns could readily be recognised by experienced Laue technologists and could easily be accommodated by a corresponding change in the computer generated pattern (Fig 5 cf Fig 4). Initially the detector was placed at 90° to the X-ray beam, as this provided a stable and easily aligned geometry and allowed good images to be obtained with low excitation potentials and tube currents (40 kV, 20mA).

Having achieved a working geometry, it was necessary to minimise the effect of random background noise, predominantly due to fluorescence in the Nickel-based alloy of the components. In the photographic method, this is achieved by the exposure: the non-random areas of the image are reinforced with time whilst the random areas are not. SCORPIO obtains a similar result by using a picture integration feature within the image processing system: a number of video frames are added, which has the same effect as the photographic exposure but takes considerably less time. At UK video rates, 25 frames per second are added. Typically, integration times are of the order of 4 to 6 seconds.

A typical image derived from a single-crystal component with the overlaid computer-generated pattern is shown on Fig 6. In this illustration a near match is demonstrated to allow visibility of both patterns.

A working system was introduced in Rolls-Royce plc, Derby, in May 1983, and the decision to offer it as a commercial product was taken shortly afterwards.

4. The Commercial History of SCORPIO and its Effect on the Later Developments

Discussion with the lead potential SCORPIO customer started early in 1984. The standard of system being offered was identical to that which had by now been proved on many thousands of components at Derby even though significant progress had already been made towards replacing the operator-controlled "pattern matching" analysis technique described above with an automatic method. This decision was based on the major concerns expressed by the customer, which centred on reliability - both in terms of downtime (seen as a major cost factor) and the dependability of the results. By offering the same standard of system as used within Rolls-Royce plc, we could provide actual data on downtime and a back-to-back comparison of SCORPIO results with the traditional method, which had been carried out as part of the proving trials.

At the same time, we were able to demonstrate progress on the automatic analysis package, which was being developed as an "add-on" to the original system without making any components redundant.

In addition to the emphasis on reliability which actually affected the sales policy rather than the technical development, the lead customer also introduced a much extended software specification which reflected the varying demands of their own customers. This was mostly concerned with the definitions of the angles which specify the crystal orientation, but also incorporated changes to the output format to include more information and an ability to specify orientations with respect to symmetry points other than (001). In addition, two programs were requested which were specific to the customer's own practices.

Whilst meeting this specification in full required an appreciable software development effort, all the changes (other than those specific to the individual customer) would similarly be requested by other customers in the USA and, thereby, improved the marketability of the system. Hence this was the first example of the commercialisation of SCORPIO influencing the technical development.

Concurrently with preparing the first commercial system for the USA, work proceeded on the automatic analysis technique.

In fact, by a coincidence, this system was first demonstrated to a representative of the USAF by two of the authors in Derby in November 1984, whilst the other was visiting the lead customer in the USA to discuss the terms of sale.

Despite this successful demonstration, the feedback from both the lead and the second potential customers still stressed that proven reliability was seen as more important than incorporating the latest developments at the earliest date - at least as far as major casting companies were concerned.

The decision was therefore taken not to offer the automatic analysis version of SCORPIO commercially until it had been used successfully inside Rolls-Royce plc for long enough for a provable track record to be established.

This decision could only have been made on the basis of direct customer contact as a competitor from the USA had by now become available and was offered from the outset with a claimed automatic analysis capability.

The original R&D objectives of the SCORPIO programme were a definite advantage in this aspect, as the automatic analysis package had been specified as an addition to the existing system without redundancy, thereby enabling customers to buy the original system with the knowledge that the later development would not make it obsolete.

Another feature which was under discussion at this time was some form of automated component loading.

Again, the customers' views were sought at an early stage and these confirmed internal advice that, whilst a semi-automated handling system would be a bonus, it would be better to concentrate on developing a fully robotic cell incorporating automatic blade identification and surface preparation to be built around SCORPIO rather than to delay this by working on an intermediate system - particularly given the importance of repeatability in component positioning.

Such a cell, known as 'ATLAS' was installed in Rolls-Royce's Derby Precision Casting Foundry late in 1987 and has subsequently been extended on the basis of production experience.

The key elements of the cell have all been demonstrated to existing SCORPIO customers and to other single crystal manufacturers who plan to work at the volumes which make automation cost effective.

Another, separate, area of application for SCORPIO is in the measurement of the grain boundary defects which may occur in single-crystal castings.

At an early stage in the commercial history of SCORPIO, it was recognised that the customers had a greater requirement for an advanced technique for the measurement of low angle grain boundary misorientations than did Rolls-Royce plc, who were concentrating, initially, on automating primary grain measurement. The misorientation requirement arises where a component contains, in fact, more than one crystal. If the axes of these crystals are closely aligned with each other, and the primary orientation is acceptable, then the mechanical properties of the component are not seriously degraded and it can be used in service. If, however, the misorientation is above pre-specified limits or (in this case more significantly) if it cannot accurately be measured, then the component must be rejected.

The reason for the high priority put onto this aspect by the USA casting companies was that they were measuring a comparatively high number of grain boundaries as a routine inspection. This was in turn the result of the nature of some of the components, which were large and of complex shape.

Grain boundaries are often evident on the blade surface in positions such as the blade platforms, which causes a problem in positioning the component for measurement.

This was particularly true of SCORPIO, where the position of the detector at 90° to the X-ray beam restricts the working space available and sometimes makes positioning the blade impossible - especially for larger components.

With the increasing number of single crystal components being manufactured and a corresponding increase in the number of large or complex parts, SCORPIO clearly needed to be able to overcome this problem.

The approach taken was to redesign the fixturing system which is used to set and maintain the alignment of the detector, the X-ray beam and the specimen. The angle between the detector axis and the X-ray beam was made variable such that the detector could be moved back closer to the traditional 'back reflection' geometry. Similarly, the component positioning fixture was also made variable, allowing its axis always to bisect the angle between the detector axis and the X-ray beam.

This change alone did not allow sufficient movement of the detector to give the full working area required (see Fig 7).

The front end of the detector was therefore redesigned to give a reduced diameter over a short length. This permitted further movement of the detector allowing for movement of the component, as shown on Fig 8.

The optimum position of the detector, for grain boundary work is a compromise between image quality, which improves as the detector is moved towards its original 90° position, and working area. In practice, the arrangement shown on Fig 8 is normally employed. This offers the maximum angle consistent with allowing free movement of the component perpendicular to its own axis. The variable geometry fixtures, however, allow further movement where required for particularly awkward components.

One major advantage of an X-ray detector refreshed at video rate, such as the X-ray television camera used in SCORPIO, is that the image can be displayed "live" - ie in true real-time. This is highly important in the grain boundary work for locating the exact position of the boundary. In the past, the component would be set using either a pointer or visual alignment such that the X-rays were incident on one grain. Not only is this slow and potentially inaccurate, but it cannot be used where it is essential to analyse the area very close to the boundary - for example where very small grains known as striations can exist. It was quite clear that an easy method of analysing striations was strongly desired.

Using the real-time nature of the image and a movable component fixture (driven by stepper motors), SCORPIO allows the user to search for and locate the boundary simply by watching the image on the monitor. The frame averaging mode of the image processor (Quantel Intellect 100 on early systems and Crystal Sapphire on later units) offers a significant level of noise reduction whilst maintaining a sufficiently fast response to movement for the system still to be considered as operating in real time.

In practice, this development of SCORPIO has successfully measured misorientations on a number of components, both from within Rolls-Royce plc and from a Customer, which could not have been measured by the earlier versions of the system or easily by film techniques. Hence the combination of the modified working geometry with real-time boundary location not only allows the cost savings associated with SCORPIO to be extended to grain boundary analysis but also introduces further savings due to reduced scrap where components could not be measured using film.

5. Future Developments

The customers' requirement for assured product support has led to Rolls-Royce plc transferring the marketing and service of SCORPIO to Rolls-Royce MatEval Limited, a wholly-owned subsidiary specialising in advanced non-destructive testing.

Technical development of the system will nevertheless be retained within Rolls-Royce plc, and will primarily be driven by the requirements of the Precision Casting Foundry.

The current direction of research is towards the location and measurement of sub-surface grains, ie, those which do not lead to a visible grain boundary on the surface which can be analysed using present techniques.

The involvement of Rolls-Royce MatEval Limited may, however, identify new applications for SCORPIO in markets other than gas turbine aeroengine components or lead to an increase in capability in the existing market. A method for correcting for orientation effects on the ultrasonic measurement of blade wall thicknesses and obtaining additional metallurgical information from Debye-Scherrer patterns are examples of the latter.

6. Conclusion

SCORPIO is an example of the application of technology normally applied to radioscopy into the field of X-ray diffraction. This involved developments both in the detector and in the analysis software.

The project has been very successful technically, demonstrating considerable cost savings within Rolls-Royce plc and, as a result, has generated an equally successful commercial product.

Because of the industrial nature of the customers, the market factors deciding purchase have been reliability and proven performance rather than state-of-the-art technology and this has implications not only for future developments of SCORPIO but for other radioscopy-based products in this market.

There is potential to develop SCORPIO further both within its original area of application and into new fields, and this is being actively pursued.

REFERENCES

Ref 1: From Research to Cost-Effective Directional Solidification and Single Crystal Production - An Integrated Approach.

G J S Higginbotham, Rolls-Royce plc, Materials and Design, Vol VIII, No 1, Jan 1987.

ACKNOWLEDGMENTS

The publishers are grateful to Messrs Rolls-Royce plc for permission to publish this paper.

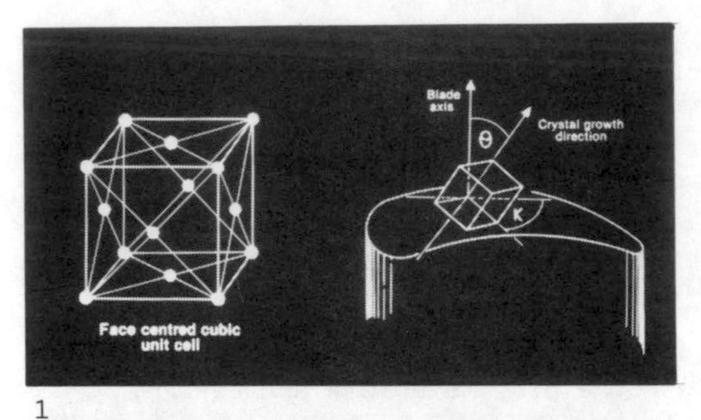

1 Crystal structure and relationship to the turbine blade.

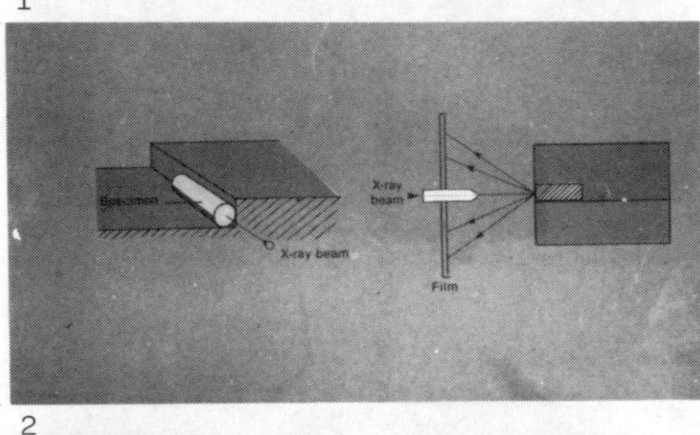

2 Standard Back Reflection Geometry.

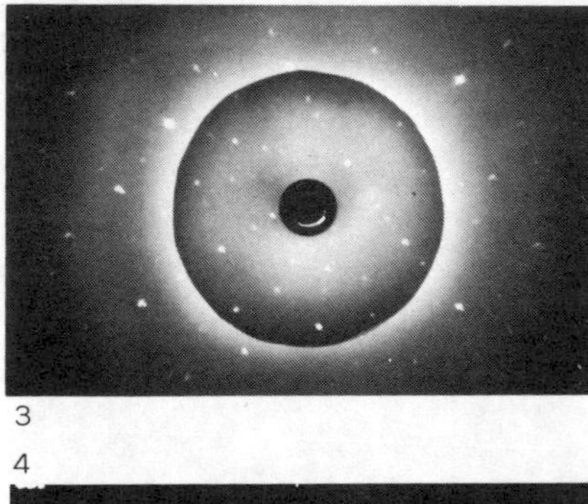

3 Laue Film in Standard back reflection.

4 Calculated Laue Pattern at origin. Standard back reflection geometry.

5 Calculated pattern at origin. Inclined geometry.

6 Integrated image with calculated 001 Pattern.

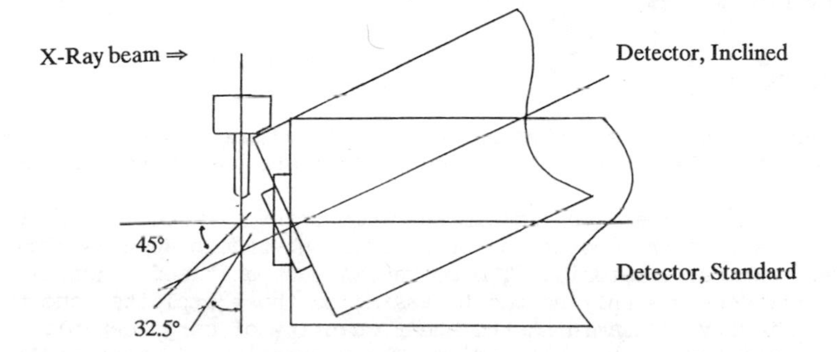

Figure 7 - Effect of Variable Geometry on Working Area

By decreasing the angle between the X-ray beam and the detector axis, the available working area is increased. In order to maximise this effect, the specimen is located further from the collimator, and the detector-specimen separation is increased to 40 mm. The working area is still, however, limited by contact between the detector and the collimator support.

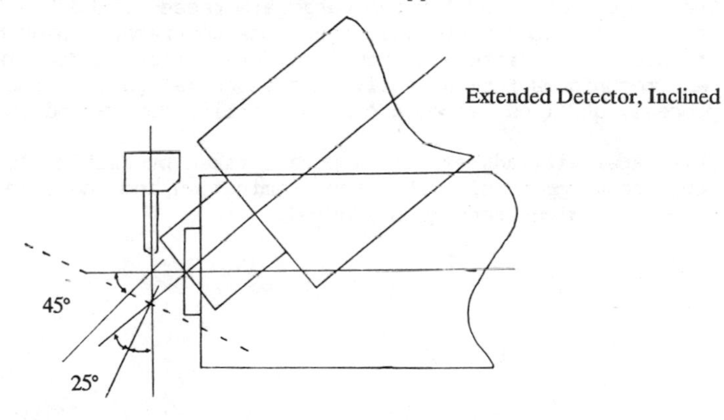

Figure 8 - Effect of Reduced Frontal Area on Working Area

By decreasing the frontal area of the detector, as shown, contact between the detector and the collimator support is avoided. This allows the angle between the X-ray beam and the detector axis to be reduced further until a specimen can be tracked across the X-ray beam, as shown, without contact with the detector. This is the condition required for real-time grain boundary location.

NON-INTRUSIVE EXAMINATION OF CARGO CONTAINERS

Mr D.D. WATERS

ABSTRACT

Over recent years, international trade and the consequential movements of materials across international frontiers has increased significantly.

With the increase in legitimate cargo traffic came the inevitable increase in transportation of illegal substances such as drugs, weapons and explosive material. The convenience of unitised loads like ISO containers has only served to assist in these exploits, due to the difficulty of examining the sheer quantity of cargo capable of being transported, using this medium. The inspection of unitised loads by customs or security staff has to date been very labour intensive, as well as often resulting in damage to produce or delays in shipments reaching the consignee. In addition, such inspection is often performed in only a cursory manner.

British Aerospace, Dynamics Division, has developed a system of non-intrusive examination of cargo containers employing two complementary high technology techniques. To "smell" any illicit substances present, the vapours given off by the cargo are passed through a tandem quad-rupole mass spectrometer. To "see" the contraband, high energy X-rays are used to generate a conventional absorption shadow. Image enhance-ment techniques form an active and essential part of the examination process, utilized by operators to identify contraband items.

This paper will address the approach taken by British Aerospace to the novel requirement of bulk cargo examination and the role played by the various imaging techniques adopted.

British Aerospace plc, Dynamics Division, CSS Department,
Downshire Way, Brackness , Berkshire, RG12 1QL

TOMOGRAPHIC IMAGES FROM REAL-TIME RADIOGRAPHY EQUIPMENT

S.F. BURCH

ABSTRACT

Since the development by Hounsfield of the first commercial scanner in the early 1970's, the advantages of computer-assisted tomography (CAT) over conventional radiography were rapidly recognised in medicine, where the technique is now in widespread and routine use. The main advantage of CAT scanning is that a true cross-sectional image is obtained, instead of the shadow-graph obtained with conventional radiography. This is most useful when inspecting complex objects.

In contrast to the medical field, CAT scanning has been slow to be developed as a NDT technique for a number of reasons, including the high cost of the necessary equipment and the length of time required for inspection. However, systems for real-time radiography, complete with computers for image processing, are now being increasingly used in NDT.

Recent work at Harwell has shown that with specially developed software, these real-time radiography systems can readily be adapted to obtain high-quality tomographic images. The only additional equipment required is a means of rotating the component through 180°. Alternatively, if the object under inspection cannot be moved, the X-ray source and imaging system can be rotated together around the object. Another advantage of this novel NDT method for acquiring tomographic images is that the two-dimensional nature of the real-time imaging system can be exploited to give multiple tomographic cross-sections at different heights through the specimen, all derived from a single rotation of the object. Thus use of a real-time radiography system for obtaining tomographic images reduces both inspection time and equipment costs.

In NDT, tomography is probably most useful for examination of the internal details of complex structures or components, and also for the measurement of the dimensions of complex shaped flaws, especially voids and inclusions. Imaging of arbitrarily oriented planar defects and volumetric flaws in welds (particularly those in pipes) could be another promising application area for tomography.

National NDT Centre, Harwell Laboratory, Oxon. OX11 ORA

XB 2331634 9